wellcome collection

WELLCOME COLLECTION publishes thought-provoking books exploring health and human experience, in partnership with leading independent publisher Profile Books.

WELLCOME COLLECTION is a free museum and library that aims to challenge how we think and feel about health by connecting science, medicine, life and art, through exhibitions, collections, live programming, and more. It is part of Wellcome, a global charitable foundation that supports science to solve urgent health challenges, with a focus on mental health, infectious diseases and climate.

wellcomecollection.org

Nine Minds

Nine Minds

Inner Lives on the Spectrum

Daniel Tammet

wellcome
collection

Profile Books

First published in Great Britain in 2024 by
Profile Books Ltd
29 Cloth Fair
London
EC1A 7JQ
www.profilebooks.com

Published in association with Wellcome Collection

**wellcome
collection**

83 Euston Road
London NW1 2BE
www.wellcomecollection.org

1 3 5 7 9 10 8 6 4 2

Typeset in FreightText by MacGuru Ltd
Printed and bound in Great Britain by
Clays Ltd, Elcograf S.p.A.

A CIP catalogue record for this book is available from the British Library.

ISBN 978 1 80081 111 9
eISBN 978 1 80081 112 6

FSC
www.fsc.org
MIX
Paper | Supporting
responsible forestry
FSC® C018072

Contents

Author's Note

This is a book about the neurodivergent present, its past and possible futures, as told through the true stories of nine contemporary men and women on the autism spectrum. They come from England, Wales and Ireland; Canada, Australia and the United States; from France, Nigeria and Japan. They are children of the nineties and the eighties, of the seventies, sixties, fifties and forties. They have found fame in Hollywood, confronted head-on the world's violence, earned a doctorate in psychology, entered national politics, solved a homicide case, performed orthopaedic surgery, published a breakout novel, learned to see with the ears and to speak through a computer device. Together they form a unique group portrait of neurodiversity.

In collecting these stories I have thought about the many years of medical progress and societal change that made this project possible. Increasingly specialists understand autism less in terms of disorder, a problem to be solved, and more as a natural cognitive difference – infinitely variable – found in between 1–2 per cent of the general population. It was not so long ago, however, that these lives were deemed unfit for literature; if they went into print at all, it was often only as a list of symptoms in some doctor's case study. A reader could be forgiven then for believing that they possessed no vivid hopes or fears, no dreams or sense of destiny, none of the depth and complexity on which a universal story depends. Of course, in this they were not alone: LGBT and Black stories, for instance, were for a long time similarly erased or marginalised. If, today, these and other minorities and minoritised communities are finding their voice and rightful place on bookshelves, the significant gaps where neurodivergent stories should be, while narrowing, still remain. It is precisely in order to fill such a gap that this book exists.

Over the past twenty years now I have written the stories, beginning with my own, of those who perceive the world in radically different ways. In that time my writing has evolved across genres – memoir, essay, fiction, poetry, literary reportage – the better to capture and illuminate for the general reader the many intricacies of the neurodiverse experience. I am ever grateful to all those who entrust their stories to me, who honour me with their faith that I will locate the form and the words that I hope can do them justice. As I work to recreate their lives on the page, drawing on extensive research, in-depth interviews and my writer's intuition to set scenes, articulate thoughts and reconstruct dialogue, my goal is that they become characters but never caricatures. I intend to show their layers, their capacity to grow and change, their quest for meaning. Occasionally I show sides of themselves they might never have noticed or understood before.

Nine Minds was researched and written over a period of four years, 2019 to 2023, based on hundreds of hours of conversations. Coinciding with the Covid pandemic, these moving and fascinating exchanges took place over email and video call – a mode of communication often privileged, as it happens, by neurodivergent people. The men and women I reached out to had previously spoken in the media about their neurodiversity, which in most cases is how I first came across their stories. From the outset, as I listened, asked questions and scribbled a mountain of notes, my ambition was to recreate the rich inner worlds they described so precisely and evocatively (to which end, my explicit presence in these narratives, while varying from one to the next, is minimal). Worlds so much richer than the dry, bland accounts that continue to appear in print about minds on the spectrum, in texts captive to neurotypical ideas of autism written in neurotypical words. Where, for example, a scientific article might mention 'highly restricted, fixated interests', the men and women I exchanged with spoke instead of their 'passions'; where a press report would refer to a neurodivergent man's 'eccentricity', I discerned rather his willingness to transgress social codes.

Evading such limiting clichés, defying outdated prejudices, the nine minds that I portray testify each in their own way to the singular power and beauty of the autistic imagination, and to the daring freedom with which they invent their lives.

Vaughan

'And of course, each fracture has its own personality,' Vaughan said to the intern beside him, halting at a bed in the orthopaedic unit of South Health Campus. 'Let's see what we have here, for example, shall we?'

The elderly inpatient gamely lifted her left arm to both men, as if on cue. The bony arm and transparent skin added to the general impression of great age, though in fact she was only five years older than Vaughan – seventy-nine.

Vaughan took in the bruised hand, reckoned the impairment, noted the occasional flinch. He sensed the sadness in those downcast fingers; how dejected they looked.

'A nasty fall,' he said to his young colleague. 'We get a fair few like them this time of year. Optimists raring to get out and about, mistaking April here for spring.'

The trainee surgeon had been staring thoughtfully at the ailing hand and wrist. 'Do you even get spring in Calgary?' he asked quietly. His accent was American.

Young surgeons, and getting ever younger, came from all over to train under Vaughan, who was known as one of the very best hand and wrist surgeons around.

The patient said, 'Black ice in the parking lot.'

'That would do it,' said Vaughan. 'You have osteoporosis, I assume?' He assumed right.

The woman sat up as she listened to the older surgeon say to the younger, 'What are your thoughts?'

'Distal radius fracture.'

'Radiographs are normal,' Vaughan said. He was testing the American.

'Umm,' said the trainee. 'Yes, but distal radius and scaphoid fractures can sometimes be radiographically occult.'

This was good. 'Why might we think that's the case here?' Vaughan prodded.

'The patient's age and sex. Osteoporosis.' And together these factors heightened the clinical suspicion for fracture.

'Very good. Next step?'

'CT or MRI without IV contrast to exclude or confirm fracture.'

There'd been no MRI back when Vaughan was starting out. His own mentors had had to rely on the incomplete picture given by X-rays and physical exams.

'Or cast the arm and repeat radiographs in ten to fourteen days.'

At that moment the woman leaned back on her pillow and the mentor and his young charge reassured her and lowered their voices as they left the unit.

Vaughan had long excelled at this form of mentoring – what researchers call cognitive apprenticeship, in which thought processes are voiced and discussed and experience is shared. It was ironic how sharply this professional excellence contrasted with Vaughan's personal life, which had long been messy. Messy, he thought to himself, was an understatement. Sometimes he wondered why no cognitive apprenticeship exists for learning to be a son or a father, a husband or a human being. All his life his only choice had been to teach himself to pass as neurotypical (a word, like MRI, not in any of his old undergrad textbooks), though he hadn't always pulled it off. But his endurance had told, and in a career spanning fifty years medical advances had transformed many lives and, more recently, his own self-understanding.

Now, nearing well-earned retirement, he looked back on his life and career, took stock and followed his memories where they led him.

In another life, he thought, he'd have been a geographer. The drawing of maps, sinuous treks, modelling landforms would have filled his days. He was born in a valley, not in Canada but in a village called Llangattock – in the south of Wales – as ruggedly Welsh a landscape as you could ever hope to find, as Welsh as his surname, which was Bowen, and though he left with his family as an infant, the misty hills and the ever-changing light had become a part of him and stayed with him always thereafter.

Vaughan remembered better Walton-on-Thames, the market town south of London where his mother, a reverend's sudden widow, had found work teaching schoolchildren religious education. The transplant of the Welsh valley family to an English suburb succeeded, but not without rendering the Bowen brothers conspicuous. Their mother said things that were funny to English ears. She said 'daro' if she dropped something and what sounded like 'dew dew' for 'well, well'. Vaughan did not speak like this. His accent was his own. He only mumbled

3

and blushed when he started primary and promptly learned that he was fatherless. The English boys meant no harm by it – might their Welsh counterparts have been crueller? The boys in Walton simply meant to ask what it was like, but Vaughan had no way of answering. He'd never thought to consider it. Several of the older boys almost envied him and half regretted not being fatherless themselves – they fantasised fathers who had swollen up from the sting of a bee, sleepwalked off a cliff or been struck down by a Rolls-Royce. As if the glamour of such a passing might set a son apart.

No old man, they said, to give them a clip on the ear or worse.

Certainly Mrs Bowen knew how to hold a classroom, and at home she could tell off for two. She had four young sons to feed and clothe and she expressed her love in never-ending instructions: 'Ych a fi, go and wash your hands! Pass me your coats! Fetch some mint and apples from the garden!' She made every shilling of her salary go as far as possible.

With little money for toys, Vaughan and his brothers spent their free hours rambling about the town and outlying fields. He thrived on the fragrant air which smelled of recent rain and of grass crushed underfoot. In his memory, sunlight accompanied him across the browning grass beside the railway station as he walked parallel to the tracks. More so than his brothers he'd delighted in treading the same ground that carried these tracks for miles. The first time out here – sixty-something years ago, back when his life was only a life and not yet a story – an exiting train chugged past him bound for London. Full of sudden wonder, he stopped near the tracks and waited for the next one to pass. Presently he heard a clanking of rods and felt the air start to shudder and caught sight of the growing train fogging the air with its white puffs of smoke. He could taste the train – it tasted of smoke and hot metal and his own dry mouth.

He would have happily stood there all day until he ran out of trains to spot but he recalled then that he had a mother and dinner and a bath to be returning to.

In retrospect, it had been the beginning of everything: his whole life he could trace to that encounter with trains – so startling and stimulating. From that moment on he'd begun to catalogue data, classify, subdivide. Many an afternoon and weekend, he stood near the station and consigned all the passing trains' names and numbers, wheels and sizes to a little notepad, and the thrill never waned as the familiar, delicious smoke approached and the platform became the scene of a minutely timed drama. 'Union Castle,' he wrote in biro under 'Name' and the date – 16/4/61 – along with the locomotive's number, 35002, and its wheel arrangement, 4–6–2, while brakes groaned and a whistle flared and passengers clambered down or boarded.

He was also learning to dissect space and time, in railway stops and timetables.

Sometimes, for a treat, when family tickets were going cheap, his mother took her boys on a day trip to Southampton. 'Hurry up,' she'd shout as they ran with their bags along the platform, 'or we'll lose the train.' They ran with heavier bags in the summer, when the Pembroke Coast Express transported the Bowens from Paddington to Swansea, to the hill overlooking Mumbles Bay where the grandparents lived. As they rode, all along the track quarter-mile posts reared up and whipped past, and from his window seat Vaughan counted the seconds between the posts to gauge the speed.

He'd hardly told anyone before Anu – Anu Sharma-Niwa, his psychologist in Calgary – that one of the reasons he'd gone on to study medicine in Edinburgh was so he could thunder up and down the coast aboard the *Flying Scotsman*. The journey always swift and sleek. Now that was what he called a train! He'd catch the 10 a.m. out of King's Cross, with only the one stop in Newcastle. Sitting back, absorbing the steady hum of the diesel electric engine, watching the world roll by at 100 miles an hour.

Anu, whom he'd found online in 2012 at the collapse of his marriage of thirty-four years, proved a worthy successor to Frank, the doctor who had rescued him from his first breakdown in the seventies. She listened sedulously as Vaughan told her all about the trains and everything else besides, session after session, following which she'd found the words – words unavailable or unthinkable in Frank's day – to explain that he was a savant and in a career perfectly tailored for him. 'Autism?' he'd repeated, seated for the first time in decades on the patient's side of a desk. Autism: a retarding mental illness that renders children unable to function in society. Or so he'd been taught during his early seventies medical training. How inaccurate those textbooks had been. How misguided.

And so he had discovered in himself this enlightening autism, this savantism, at the age of sixty-three. It clarified so much, fed his self-discovery and confidence.

So that, ten years on from these early sessions with Anu, he could relate everything again to a youngish man named Daniel, corresponding freely with him, sharing all manner of details which had never before left his psychologist's office, because this Daniel Tammet, aside from being a writer, was also what doctors called an autistic savant. The writer understood things about him that others might not have. Vaughan was excited at the thought of seeing his story put into print. Then, hopefully his ex-wife, with whom he remained on good terms, would come to a clearer idea, on reading it, of the often awkward, silent, confusing man who had loved her as best he could during all those years.

Years that had rolled by at the speed of life.

The day after their rounds of the orthopaedic unit, Vaughan and the American put on gown, gloves and mask and positioned themselves around the operating table. The American observed in silence while Vaughan worked. The older surgeon's gestures were deft and graceful. His patient had been put at ease with anaesthesia, and between the surgeons and the nurse there was no distracting small talk. The masks and the music – something delicately classical playing low – heightened Vaughan's absorption in his task.

Head bowed, eyes focused, all his attention went to the slumbering hand in front of him. That morning he'd tended to a young and muscular forearm which for years had lobbed and served and sliced drop shots; in its place now lay a middle-aged thumb hampered by arthritis. Where the incision had been made, he could see past layers of skin and fat to the basal joint. The sight was familiar, blood and bone had never aroused any squeamishness in him; he was fascinated by the body's intricate networks of nerve, artery and tissue, all those inner parts that go unseen and on which our visible surfaces depend. What things of beauty, of nature's ingenuity, the violin strings that are the tendons! And the wrist bones shaped like a boat (the scaphoid), a crescent moon (the lunate), a pyramid (the tri-quetrum) – three among the twenty-seven bones in the human hand. In his mind's eye, he could picture each one of these small bones in three dimensions, he could visualise their every binding ligament and every muscle, the galvanising sparks and the irrigating scarlet threads.

'See the joint surface here?' Vaughan said to the American, as he extracted the bone fragments one by one. 'That's the arthritis.'

Minutes later, 'See here, the cartilage has all worn down.' Then, addressing the nurse, 'Give me a little traction, please.' Then, to the American again, 'Now I'm opening a channel in the trapezium.'

He was repeating the one he'd just opened in the trapezium in his mind's eye. Deep into the joint he drilled. Close by, sur-rounded by forceps and scalpels and scissors, the implant to replace the patient's lost bone shone bright. It was made of titanium – strong yet light and ductile and practically, most enviably, unbreakable.

The operation took just over an hour and was a complete suc-cess. Vaughan peeled off his scrubs and soaped his hands and smiled. He had barely stepped out from the operation room when he saw a woman approach him with a sheet of paper. He nodded when she said something about a schedule, less to signal assent than to cover his confusion. The woman thrust the sheet into his hands, turned on her heels and went back to her office. Only then did he realise she was his medical office assistant of twenty-plus years, and his face burned in embarrassment. He'd tried memorising her hairdo, and the comfortable jumpers she favoured, for all the good it had done him. At least she had been with him long enough to understand. From his earliest days, his memory for faces had been dreadful. He always imagined his assistant sitting attentively behind her desk, or busy with the phone. Without her desk, and walking to boot, he struggled to recognise her.

Sometimes he wondered whether it had been quite the same for his grandfather, this near-illiteracy when it came to reading the expression on a face.

Vaughan's resemblance to his mother's father was in no way physical. He remembered a very short man, bow-legged (rickets was his medical opinion later on). It was rather his grandfather's unusual mind that he'd inherited. A trained surveyor's feel for geometry. A talented retailer's head for figures. An eye for minute detail. Not that he understood this for a long time. John Sydenham Richards of Swansea, known in those parts as JSR, or as Papa by his grandchildren, was already an old man when the Bowens spent their summers visiting the grandparents. He was something of a local character, a staunch pillar of the community: he put the Richards into Manning, Martin and Richards, wholesalers formerly of Union Street. 'Matting, Mats and Rugs' proclaimed their slogan. They also sold linoleum, Acme wringers, Newmaid suction sweepers, paints and cloths. Inventorying would have been for Richards, the director, what trainspotting and medicine would become for his grandson.

It had never occurred to Vaughan to make these connections until quite recently – until, that is, the day back in the UK when a brother showed him one of their grandfather's many diaries. He showed him 1939. It was pocket-sized and filled with meticulous, vigorous handwriting. Every page was not only dated but also timed. Vaughan's brother flipped the pages to July, to the eighteenth, which had separate entries for 8.30 a.m., 9.15 a.m., 12.50 p.m., 3.23 p.m., 3.30 p.m., 4.45 p.m., 6.32 p.m., 6.34 p.m., 6.35 p.m., 6.37 p.m., 6.38 p.m., 6.40 p.m., 7.00 p.m., 7.10 p.m., 7.30 p.m.

On 18 July 1939 their grandfather and his wife May were holidaying in Bergen, Norway.

'4.45 p.m. Harbour of Bergen. Loads of fish being transferred to a ship for England. All motor cars on Quay appear to be American. Passed customs in shed. Walked along Quay to Hotel Rosenkrants,' he had written.

'Keep reading,' said Vaughan's brother, his voice almost hushed. 'Papa counted everything!'

'Room No 309. Lady's Gent's cloakroom. Sitting room. 3 couches. Writing table. 3 tables. 2 armchairs. 2 chairs. 1 writing stool. Telephone. Cabinet. 19 lights. 2 reading lamps. Sewing materials. 3 radiators. 2 twin beds. Bath. Wash up. Lavatory (W.C.). 4 Drinking glasses. 6 towels.'

In the day's next entry, timed 6.32 p.m., their grandfather had described going up the 'Floibanen or funicular railway' where he'd met an Australian tourist and enquired after her name, maiden name, occupation and address. (Mrs Freida Moyle. Miss Freida Walker. Calculator Bookkeeping Machine Expert. 20 Queen Street, Melbourne.) 'Beautiful view of Bergen,' he'd jotted down then, just before noting the ticket fare: '1.50 Kr each return. 3.00 Kr two persons.'

But for these diaries, passed down to his brother, Vaughan would have known nothing of his grandfather's inner life – and of how much more than blood they shared.

He thought of his grandfather's father who had launched the family business in the 1870s. His great-grandfather had left a rural hamlet for Swansea to set up as a wholesale grocer and butter merchant. Between father and enterprising son, the name of Richards had traded proudly in the city for a hundred years. Vaughan liked to think that certain autistic traits – tremendous focus, attention to specifics, imaginative somersaults – had played their part in the family's flourishing.

His mother had not inherited her father's strange mind. It seemed to Vaughan that there was more Richards in him than in his grandfather's eldest daughter. A chatty woman, his mother, always at ease with herself and other people and leery of spending much time alone. It was possible that her son's inwardness and intense gaze intimidated her. Chatty as she was, she never opened up to him. Or maybe, just maybe, she had, or had tried, and he'd simply not understood.

There were times as a boy he'd wanted her to assuage the distress, the confusion, inside him with a well-chosen sentence. He'd wanted her to make everything clear in his head so that he might breathe more easily. But the times were flat against that; very few people talked about feelings in the fifties, the early sixties. Except perhaps the gossips. Language back then was strictly policed. Always you minded your language, watched your p's and q's.

When Vaughan turned nine the distance between mother and son grew miles wider. He became a boarder at a free independent school for fatherless boys in Hertfordshire. Year-round he lodged there till he went up to Edinburgh at eighteen, returning to his family only for the long school holidays.

One summer, he returned to an empty house. He was twelve or perhaps thirteen. The holidays hadn't arrived yet in Walton-on-Thames and he walked to the school where his mother taught. She left the blackboard and told him to wait for her in home economics, where the children were busy baking bread. He was getting tall as well as lean, with a long fringe and bright eyes, and the girls had looked up and smiled as he joined them to knead the dough. No need for him to follow a recipe. Vaughan often assisted his mother in the kitchen. She baked a marvellous teisen lap – sweet and buttery with a hundred raisin eyes. Standing beside her at the counter, he would observe the flour as it snowed. 'Pass the whisk,' then 'pass the spatula,' she would say and he would pass her the one, and then the other, quick, quick. He'd hear the regular clinking in the mixing bowl. Feel the dip of a spoon. Feel important, like those Sundays when he broke the skin on the rice pudding.

The smell of the bread baking in the classroom. A warm, homely, informal smell. It tortured him, the memory of it, weeks later, as the autumn term loomed. Not even the prospect of riding the railway out of Waterloo could lift his spirits in the slightest. How he despised his school, its cold dorms and colder housemasters (with names like Clotworthy), the plummy voices which droned on and on for what seemed to him like days, the frightening rifle target practice. To say nothing of the awful beatings. And indeed not one word was breathed of any of this during visits home. Only as an adult, nearing thirty, would Vaughan start to articulate what he'd been through, the damage done to him, confiding in a doctor in the Canadian hospital where he worked after immigrating. Until then, he'd supposed the fault lay somehow with him, and felt the ordeal far too shaming in any case to ever mention.

Before this doctor, Frank, he'd dared not address any man by name. 'Sir' and 'Professor', and later 'Doctor' had been the rule: 'Dr Bowen?' 'Yes, Dr Green?' or 'Yes, Dr Smith?' And as for calling his mother by her first name, well, perish the thought!

'Call me Frank, Vaughan,' the doctor had said gently. In 1976, if memory served him right. That year, and over the following years, Frank would lead Vaughan out of the darkest caverns in his mind, just as Anu would decades later.

Even now he felt twinges of regret at losing touch with Frank after moving to another city. He had always been bad at looking people up, asking after them. He'd learned of the doctor's death in 2004 from a years-old obituary republished online. In 2004 he might have thought to call his mother in England with the news. Remember Frank? Dr Frank Coburn? Not a chance. By that time, she was always losing her train of thought.

The memory of mother's teisen lap. Where had that come from? And why did it have to remind him – of all things – of his boarding school thrashings? Spoons and spatulas. Clotworthy. Frank's kindly gaze.

Vaughan had always been dexterous – he could pick up and repair a shattered vase, shard by shard, repair a hand bone by bone. But the fragments of a mind – that was something else altogether. So hard to grasp and reassemble.

Of the thousands of patients he'd treated down the years, several had left Vaughan puzzled. In his memory, two – a young woman, and an older man – stood out most sharply.

The young woman had come in one day with a forearm needing surgery. His assistant had recognised her as a recent patient, ushered her into his office and handed him her file. Vaughan proceeded to inspect the young woman's forearm.

According to the file, he had operated on her months before, but there was a problem. She had no scar.

'Oh, that was my twin,' the young woman said.

Were the two sisters so identical, Vaughan wondered afterwards, that they had developed the exact same low bone density in the forearms? Or, had the scar on one, throwing off their symmetry, incited the other to undergo her sister's operation?

The older man – a driver in his fifties – had had his wrist crushed in a collision. The wrist had necessitated a big operation, lasting hours, but no sooner had the man's anaesthesia worn off than he discharged himself, saying only, 'I have an urgent flight.' The sole address he'd left was a box number in a Chinese city. He had no healthcare insurance so Vaughan did not get paid.

Then, one day, eighteen months later, Vaughan's assistant phoned him. 'You will never guess what just happened,' she said. Did he remember the man with the Chinese address? Well, he'd just left a bulging unmarked envelope for him with her, which she'd opened. Inside was the fattest wad of used $20 bills.

Was there anything more confounding, more impenetrable, Vaughan wondered, than the human mind?

Dr Frank Coburn was Head of Psychiatry at the University of Saskatchewan and Vaughan a young resident surgeon at the campus's teaching hospital. Vaughan was training under a British missionary whose specialty was the spine. The doctors Coburn and Bowen knew each other only in passing, as one more name on a door or a tag.

The life of the hospital was stimulating and purposeful and at times happier than the gruelling work and proximity to illness might suggest. Vaughan derived a deep satisfaction from mending bones spalled by illness and injury.

But his surgical prowess masked an inner turmoil – an early marriage, to an American student he'd met in Edinburgh, was failing fast. Her family had never approved of him; they refused to ascribe his quirks, as others did, to being British.

Fatherless from boyhood, Vaughan's notion of a husband, or a prospective husband, had been formed by the movies' square-jawed leading men. He asked himself where on earth these Bonds and Bogarts had learned their amazing insouciance, their worldliness, and presumed that the answer was the crowded and exotic bars he'd never set foot in.

He felt woefully underprepared for adult life. He tried to make sense of the 27-year-old breadwinner he had become, of the couple he formed with this young and bright American. Who was she exactly? The question weighed on him. His wife was an increasingly pressing source of bafflement: one minute she could be sitting on their sofa laughing, a beat later, tearing up. She seemed always to be telling him or pleading with him to listen. Vaughan would expend a tremendous effort to converse with her, but his remarks invariably fell flat, and when she complained he did not know why or what to say or do next. He wasn't at all big on hugs – try as he might, he would never be Bogart to her Bacall. One frustrating evening, one of many, exasperation seized his wife and drove her to yell at him, 'What's wrong with you?'

What indeed? Vaughan did not know himself. He sensed himself unravelling. Some days he went out of his mind, or rather, he went further and further within it, turning this way and that, taking wrong turns, following thoughts that grew murkier, until he felt lost and afraid.

Over the months that followed, during which his discomposure steadily increased, he trudged through his hospital rounds, ate without appetite, slept fitfully, didn't open letters, didn't return neighbours' waves, didn't call on colleagues after shifts, went from slim and fair to thin and pale to gaunt and ashen.

In his weakened state the border between present and past became porous. Years of repressed mental struggles could no longer be contained. The tiniest reminder of his past caused Vaughan's throat to contract abruptly: a stranger's schoolmaster-like gait, or the overheard words of some argument between boys, at other times simply the scent of rain like the rain in Walton would trouble him no end. A few footsteps, a mouthful of words, a hint of a downpour – all it might take to set him off, even if they amounted to nothing more or in fact were only his imagination, which pained him all the same and just as much.

Vaughan had heard good things from his patients about Dr Coburn. But still he refrained from acting until one day after a long shift when the still lucid part of him telephoned up to the hospital's fifth floor and told Coburn's secretary that it was urgent.

'I told the lady on the phone that it was for one of my orthopaedic patients,' Vaughan explained to the psychiatrist. 'The fact is, I'm the person who needs to consult you.' And then, encouraged by a nod, he started to ramble. After a while his feeble voice trailed off. Eventually his unfocused eyes rose to meet the doctor's short grey beard and thick glasses and high bald forehead.

'You were miles away there, Vaughan.'

'Dr Coburn?'

'Call me Frank, Vaughan.'

*

In Frank's office silence was for Vaughan not a rebuke but an encouragement. In the privacy offered by its bare walls he could speak his mind. He at last unburdened himself, talking freely, taking a decade of nightmares and inexplicable headaches up to that room on the fifth floor. He described how some days he felt like he was inside a chill, black tunnel where he saw not the faintest pinprick of future light.

Frank tried him on tranylcypromine for the depression and lithium for the mood swings but far better than either of these, and without their side effects, proved to be the talking. Much of the talk returned to the English boarding school Vaughan had long attended. Vaughan described how he'd followed the other boarders' example of putting on a brave face and voice at all times. If some of the classmates had teased him for his aloofness, many more had ignored him. With his slender, agile fingers he'd played first flute in the school orchestra – the regular rehearsals, along with the chapel and library, had kept him out of the way of most bullies.

But there had been no getting away from the masters.

'They weren't all rotten,' said Vaughan. Those who taught the sciences, in particular, had found in him an able, responsive student. And often in the middle of geography he'd experienced a lightness rising in his chest like bread in a hot oven.

Taking up his pipe, drawing on it, Frank managed to get Vaughan on to the subject of the Colonel. A few times before, he had mentioned this man only to hastily switch to something else.

The Colonel had been Vaughan's housemaster when he entered sixth form, Frank learned. Vaughan had soon become the object of this Colonel's volcanic temper; years later, he could still hear him barking, 'Bowen!' The teenager would respond too slowly to some comment. Or play too quietly in the marching band. He would look the wrong way or say the wrong thing. Whatever the excuse, he'd jump out of his skin at the Colonel's bark and flinch at what was coming. Those big, ugly, bulging veins on the fist gripping the rattan cane.

The burning sting of it.

Long, throbbing indentations on his back and buttocks.

As if the Colonel intended to pound out of him his difference.

Beat out of him everything that made Vaughan Vaughan.

The Colonel drunk on his own anger, seeing double.

When, oh when, would the whistling cane stop?

For two years, all through sixth form, far more beatings than Vaughan cared to recall. They had left their indelible mark on him. Regardless of the years, then decades, that elapsed, he would be able to relive the scene as if it were yesterday. The Colonel would be long dead by now but still he continued to cast his violent shadow over Vaughan's thoughts. Nevertheless, and thanks to Frank, Vaughan had acquired means to discern and clamber out of the shadow.

As he spoke and Frank listened, Vaughan found himself thinking how lucky he was to be working at this hospital in Saskatchewan, among the prairies where he had spent his gap year as a farmhand. The summer before that year, by a similar twist of fate, Vaughan had discovered his vocation on a hiking holiday in Wales. A rare friend at the boarding school had accompanied him, and as they made their way across the limestone cliffs in Gower each tossed out ideas about their future.

'I'm going to be a doctor,' his mate said rather proudly. His father was a physician in the Royal Army Medical Corps, a man who had travelled far and wide and seen service in places that sounded brimful of adventure. The son's evident pride could not help but touch Vaughan, and as he walked beside his friend he let himself imagine what it might be like to live and work far away overseas. The thought of healing others, he realised, appealed to him, for reasons he would be unable to explain fully to his friend or even to himself. And just like that, Vaughan began to wonder whether he too should follow in this unknown man's footsteps. By the time he came back to Walton his decision was firm. He would abandon his plans to enrol in geography; he would bring his youthful intelligence to bear on the human body rather than on the earth. The former, he intuited, would absorb his mind most completely.

For all Frank's efforts on the fifth floor, Vaughan's health continued to deteriorate. After his wife moved out, he was admitted to the hospital's psychiatric unit. Fortunately his fellow surgeons were understanding. They would wait until he could resume his service. At his lowest ebb, Vaughan became for a brief time catatonic, losing the power of speech, before improving enough to return to Frank's office and then to his medical duties.

His recovery was slow, however, and there would be relapses. Frank, faced with Vaughan's third admission, invited him into his home instead. Mrs Coburn made tea as the two men settled into armchairs and let the radio – *As It Happens* – do all the talking. Sitting back, the family's red setter at their feet, they could have been father and son.

When Vaughan was well enough, the Coburns drove him to their summer cabin on Wakaw Lake. The green of poplars rested his eyes, the breadth of blue sky buoyed his spirits, and all around him a soothing peace reigned supreme. When Frank talked, as they strolled beside the shining lake, or in the cooler evenings as they kept warm before a crackling wood stove, he said nothing about the hospital. Instead he related light, amusing stories of his children's time at camp.

By the end of Vaughan's month with the Coburns, his physical and mental health had gone from strength to strength. He felt up to resuming surgery at the hospital. Frank was supportive but remained vigilant. There was still, he cautioned Vaughan, a long way to go. And indeed Vaughan might have regressed once again had Frank not called Vaughan's mother in England and alerted her to the depth of her son's problems.

Vaughan himself hadn't managed to tell his mother much about his plight; whenever he'd called long-distance she'd spent half the time fretting aloud about how expensive each of the minutes must be. As soon as she came off the phone with Frank, she brought forward the flight she had already booked for the off-season. She flew over on the next available plane and for several months set up quarters in her son's apartment.

There was only so much she could get out of him – Vaughan had never been a great talker. He was relieved when, with his permission, she took her many questions to Frank. One sunny afternoon, when she and Vaughan had come out to the cabin, Frank took her out in his canoe on the lake. They were gone for quite some time.

Frank may have saved Vaughan's life; certainly, he salvaged his career. And the young surgeon gained further stability when, following his divorce, he met and later married the operating-room nurse with whom he would raise a son and daughter.

Vaughan, by the 1980s, was performing regular operations in a country where there were few hand and wrist specialists. He was admired by his peers; they'd witnessed him innovate techniques to mend the smallest bones and graft skin. Soon he was earning a reputation as *the* hand and wrist man to be consulted. Patients came to him from miles around. Quite a number were tanned farmers from the surrounding prairies, their clothes and limbs dramatically snatched by a tractor's rotating shaft, rushed in and hoping to be reunited with a severed thumb or fingers.

'It pretty near tore my whole hand off,' they'd grumble in a voice husky with pain and embarrassment.

Other men, when winter came, had reached inside a clogged snowblower without thinking. Vaughan repaired each mangled hand, skilfully replanting the amputated digits, fusing together the tiny veins so that the blood went only where Mother Nature intended.

Women arrived at his hospital with different complaints. Pregnancy induced in some a tingling numbness in the fingers. Vaughan explained that the nerve passing through the wrist's carpal tunnel had become compressed by the body's swelling. He reassured them that this compression usually ceased in the weeks and months after delivery.

'But if ever it persists, or worsens, then you must come back and see me,' said Vaughan. 'You mustn't wait. We will find the right treatment for you.'

When presented with stiff and swollen hands by older women he never presumed, just because these patients were getting on, that their discomfort was ageing's due. As Vaughan examined them intently and asked many thoughtful questions, it struck the women how undivided his attention was. They were unused to a surgeon taking so seriously a woman's pain, her female ailments. Both men and women appreciated how courteous and unassuming he was.

After practising surgery for a time in Saskatoon, in 1993 Vaughan set up the Hand Program at Toronto Western Hospital. His career later took him to Stanford University and later still to Calgary.

Vaughan had pictures in his mind of his white-haired mother holding court in Norfolk. She had retired there in the eighties to live near her two older sons. Vaughan and his wife and children, whenever they'd been over in the UK, had called on her. It had been a great help to him, having a wife who always knew what to say at social gatherings.

'Oh, these are fabulous,' he recalled his wife saying of his mother's biscuits which were sending their crumbs everywhere.

'Where are my manners?' exclaimed his mother, who had been pouring milk for the tea. 'I'll fetch the plates.' No, no, she didn't need any help, she insisted, shooing her daughter-in-law away from the kitchen. Having returned with the plates, she sank low into her armchair and told them stories about the village. Then she gave an account of a cruise she had taken the summer before last – or had it been the summer before that? – to the Middle East. Vaughan knew that he ought to ask his mother some polite thing or other about her cruise but he wasn't quite sure what.

'Must have been nice and hot over there,' said his wife.

'You can say that again.'

'Did you get seasick at all?'

'Oh, no. I was too busy for that.' There had been nightly lectures on the ship, she added, like the one given by a professor on Greek mythology. Zeus. The nine Muses. The Minotaur. Very informative.

Vaughan was content to leave the conversation to the two women. It was pleasant to listen to his mother's still-strong voice, her whole being seeming to shout with her usual vitality. But then it occurred to him that his mother was repeating herself, which was unlike her. She was back to the exact same stories about the village.

'Sorry, but we have to be getting back,' he interrupted.

Only some while after that, on another day over in Norfolk, did it become clear to Vaughan that there was something very wrong with his mother. She'd made no fuss then when he went to the kitchen for the crockery and milk. When he opened the fridge door, he saw that the milk wasn't there. The shelves for the cheese and butter, the ones for meat or fish, and the bottom drawer for the fruit and vegetables, were also empty.

He'd flown to Canada by the time the results of his mother's neurological exams came back. The dreaded 'A' word. The next time he had seen her in Norfolk she was living in residential care. He'd flown over on his own, on one of those packed flights that made his temples throb. What a relief, then, arriving at the home, to discover the converted Georgian mansion that housed it, majestic calm in stone form and set in acres of parkland.

Shown around by a member of staff, he went to the large, light-giving windows. The country views, he thought, would have recommended the place to his older brother who had chosen the home.

Their mother's room was situated at the rear, in a separate wing built of brick for the residents with dementia. The voice of Vera Lynn – forever the voice of a bright young up-and-comer – carried down the corridors. Along the walls, old posters of

Cunard cruises to New York invited reverie and reminiscence. On this and every visit that followed to this wing, Vaughan would step out of 1999 (or 2003 or 2007, the final time) and into the forties.

The forties had coincided with his mother's youth, her early years as a wife and mother, and hearing the period's songs, viewing its posters, helped to revive her. Momentarily, she recovered possession of her confidence, her old ease surfaced. She might respond sensibly to some remark and move around with renewed grace. But, always, Vaughan noticed beneath the grace the tremendous effort, and he saw himself in that effort. The minute after, that ease – and with it the mother he had always known – would be gone.

The final time he had sat with her, she was ninety years old and she was nine years old. She was talking to him in the incomprehensible Welsh she'd used with her parents in Swansea. From the reclining chair in her room, his mother was telling him something breathily – an unabating singsong, deferential. He realised then that he was her father – she was addressing her father. How he wished he could understand her.

A hand on her lap grew agitated and he reached over and squeezed the plump cushion of her palm in reassurance. He was searching his mind for the only Welsh he had, words he'd taught himself for this moment.

Dwi'n caru ti.

I love you.

A few days ago a calendar reminded Vaughan of his forthcoming retirement. He hadn't needed any reminding but there it was in black and white: 26 June 2024. Fifty years. Half a century to the day since he'd graduated with his Edinburgh medical degree.

He'd always enjoyed looking ahead, not only days or weeks but into the following year, looking ahead and seeing all the lined-up events that promised to keep his life full and bustling. Whereas spring 2023 had yet to reach Calgary (still treadmill weather here in April), already in his mind he was halfway into 2024.

His operating days were not over just yet, he thought. He was good for one more year at the hospital. His body in shape, fit enough to run marathons and compete internationally in duathlons. They helped to clear his head.

Today was Monday. Vaughan was up by 4 a.m., as was his habit. The writing of case reports monopolised his early mornings, after which he got into his office by eight. Monday was consultations day. These consultations involved new patients and for this reason tended to overrun. Vaughan liked to take his time with each patient, to inspect every part, each nook and cranny of a person's medical history. To leave no stone unturned.

Patients, he knew from experience, rarely volunteered the most useful information about their illnesses. It took Vaughan's probing questions to gently winkle these details out of them. No, they did not experience any wrist pain. Yes, they sometimes felt a stiffness in the small joints. Yes, the stiffness was worse in the morning. No, they were not diabetic. Then he would inspect their fingers and close his own around a pen and fill in the long form in their file with the necessary particulars.

They were like anyone else, the men and women who came each Monday into his office, never thinking about their hands until compelled by illness or accident. All those years during which they mistook a phone's rising to the ear and a jar's unscrewing and a hardcover's page-turning for natural events, then a strange twinge or a sudden ache would make the book a brick, the jar a safe, the phone a wet bar of soap.

What kind of pain, Vaughan would want to know. But the deep intimacy of their pain made his patients inarticulate. Often they could only compare it to another kind. Like a toothache, one man might say. Like a raging toothache, but in the knuckles.

For some patients, the next step would be a splint, or hand rehabilitation exercises. For others, further examinations – a scan or blood test. Occasionally, Vaughan undid a misdiagnosis – recognising personal variations on an anatomical feature as normal and only simulating disease.

After another long Monday in his office, in his thoughts Vaughan returned to the summer of 2024. His near-future retirement. Perhaps he would travel to Llangattock, his birth-place, to mark the occasion. He could see himself doing that. He imagined himself walking down the brow of the hill to join a guide and explore the caves beneath, the labyrinthine passage-ways, among Europe's most extensive. Relentlessly he would grapple through them, tackling their elusive twists and con-founding turns, feeling his way along the calcite walls in the semi-dark as spelunkers do. He would not falter. He would feel like he had been here many times before.

Kana

Dear Ms Seiko Noda, Minister of Loneliness. So began the letter Kana had spent several days writing in her head (horizontally, and left to right, the letter being in English, the language she preferred to think in) and continued, after the necessary preliminaries:

I applaud your ministry's recent creation and its aim to tackle the spiralling problem of loneliness in the country.

On the government's website, I notice that it does not mention who might be more vulnerable to loneliness. Research has shown that 'disabled' people can be lonelier than 'non-disabled', autistic people particularly so. Autistic people do not 'have a disability', but they are 'disabled' when others around them do not understand their differently wired minds nor accommodate for their needs. Making accommodations confers on them no additional merits, but simply permits them to be on a level playing field with everyone else.

A lack of understanding from others leads to loneliness, just as much as the absence of social relationships. Addressing this would go a long way towards alleviating loneliness in the nation. This could include diminishing the stigma around autism in Japan and bringing the correct knowledge of autism and autistic loneliness to the wider society . . .

Where was she now? Nowhere. In the no-woman's land between sleep and waking. She opened her eyes, looked up at the ceiling, down at Sky. No, wait, that was impossible. Sky was in heaven. She closed tight and then opened her eyes again, and saw Levi. The schnauzer puppy wagged her white tail as Kana hauled herself out of bed.

As always, she was up with the first pink of dawn and the city's sparrows she heard from her window as they balanced on the telephone wires, chirping. As she looked out, she remembered that in her dream she'd been a mouse, a dancing mouse in a circus. She recalled distinctly her scurrying to reach the mouse troupe from which she had been separated for some unknown reason. Scurrying, her mouse's heart hammering, because the troupe would be waiting to start. They would not start their dancing without her.

Slippers padded along the corridor, a soft tap at the door preceded its opening, and her mother smiled into the bedroom.

'The tea's ready,' Hiromi said.

Despite her time in America, and many months in Britain, Kana still took her tea green. No milk or sugar.

On her way to the kitchen she passed through the living room. Long and wide as six tatami mats, the room seemed more spacious since she and Hiromi had finished packing most of their belongings into boxes. It was September 2021, and they were leaving the mainland and their home of thirty years, Utsunomiya, for Okinawa. They were moving to an apartment near the American Village and the harbour and counting down the days until their departure. They would take a taxi to the airport, saying a last goodbye to the paddies, cornfields and orchards, whose changes rang in the seasons. Farewell to the mountain views and the smell of cows through the car windows as they drove.

Thirty years of life slimmed down to a dozen or so boxes. Hiromi was a single parent, Kana an only child. There was hardly anything, or anyone, to keep them here. Kana's father, who had left their lives years ago, was helping to pay for the move. Her mother, a make-up artist turned aesthetician, would find new clients on the island.

The two women sat down to breakfast: bagels, for Kana, and *amazaki*, a fermented rice drink, for Hiromi. They hadn't yet packed away their chairs and table.

'A writer contacted me the other day about a book he's working on,' said Kana. 'A British man living in Paris.' She was familiar with his work. She gave his name in Japanese for her mother's benefit: Danieru Tametto.

What sort of books had this Tametto-san written, Hiromi was curious to know, and why was he contacting her. 'Is it something to do with your research?'

Kana flushed; she nodded. 'Research' was the kind of word that sounded fine when she said it but pretentious when others did. She was twenty-seven years old, and while she felt strongly about her work, she was the last person who would ever make a fuss about it. Which was why the enquiries from this British writer, like those from the American reporter before him, had been as big a surprise to her as they were to her mother. A reassurance, too, that she really might be on to something.

She was a researcher in loneliness. She measured and

dissected it with considerable zeal, even passion, because it was a young field of research, fast-expanding, increasingly vital, and also because she had often known first-hand the ache of feeling alone. If anyone – the British writer or the American reporter or someone else – were to ask her how she measured a thing like loneliness, she could answer: the same way you measure the wind. By its observable effects on our world. You could identify and grade the various forms of loneliness, just like we identify and grade a dozen kinds of wind – running from light air and fresh breeze to gale and hurricane.

'0' – Contentment – being wholly at ease in the world

...

'3' – Mild isolation – aloneness is noticed regularly, living and work spaces seem excessively large

'4' – Moderate isolation – aloneness is unpleasant like body odour, days feel very long

...

'6' – Estrangement – sense of not belonging, being unlike others, connection is difficult

...

'8' – Severe exclusion – sensation of being cut off from others by an invisible wall

...

'10' – Forsakenness – empties life of meaning, all possibility of connection seems lost

Daughter and mother spent the rest of breakfast talking about Kana's research. 'I know how important this is to you,' Hiromi said. 'Your life's work.'

Kana

*

Kana's present work had begun three years earlier with an application letter for the research position of her dreams, at University College, London. After two weeks of waiting (and pacing, and nail biting), the centre's response seemed on track to becoming the slowest in the history of email and Kana's hopes were oh-so-close to evaporating. And then, well, you can fill in the rest. Fully worth the wait, the mail that came back from Dr Laura Crane. And, as it proved, a turning point.

During their video conference Laura had smiled a lot and called Kana's CV impressive. A science degree from North-eastern University and a Master's in Counseling Theory from Boston College. A distinction received in her Postgraduate Certification in Autism and Asperger's Syndrome at Sheffield Hallam University.

'I see that you would like to investigate loneliness in autistic adults using mixed methods during your PhD research with us at CRAE. Your input as a researcher with lived experience of autism will be especially valuable to us.'

This was what had attracted Kana to CRAE – the Centre for Research in Autism and Education – one of the few sites in the world where neurotypical and autistic scholars worked together to enhance science's understanding of autism. The team had a core principle: that autistic people should be central to the production of knowledge about the condition.

'We found your choice of research topic very interesting,' Laura continued. 'As you know, many scientists have long believed that autistic people prefer to be on their own and therefore rarely, if ever, feel lonely.'

These beliefs, Kana knew only too well, were flat-out wrong.

But for a surprising amount of years, the scientists, all wrapped up in their theories, had seldom thought to ask their subjects how they were actually feeling. When they had, they used curious phrasing that could befuddle. Do you feel in tune with other people? In tune? Yes, in tune. No, I don't feel in tune. (Under their breath, adding, Do I look like a musical instrument?) And so the scientist, taking up his clipboard, would tick 'no', and neither he nor the subject came out of this exchange any the wiser.

'We are based at Gordon Square, close to King's Cross', added Laura, before warning that their offices weren't the best environment for neurodivergent colleagues. 'It's an old building, but being listable there isn't much that can be done to make where we work more comfortable. We're on the fourth floor, but to avoid walking through other people's workspaces it can be necessary to head down to the second and along a corridor before going up another staircase. Like a maze. And we're on a busy road, often with construction work nearby. It can get very noisy in the summer with the windows open. No air conditioning unfortunately.'

On the plus side, the Centre was close to everything. Shops and markets. Libraries. Transport links. Her postgrad student accommodation. The staff was small, work hours flexible and any social events up to her to take or leave. And the building had a certain charm, Kana found when she arrived, compared with the concrete of her home town. Yellow stock bricks, decorative ironwork – that sort of charm. Not to mention the adjoining public gardens where she ate her lunch with the squirrels. A local benefactor fixed his bronze gaze on her as she passed the iron railings. Some days the bald statue wore a pigeon for a wig, Mohawk style.

Kana was elated. More than elated – ecstatic. Here I am! she told herself, and it was as though she could feel those words rushing to culminate in an exclamation mark. In London, doing what she'd spent the past several years in the States and Britain preparing to do. How many other neurodivergent researchers had an opportunity like this, to research and publish, she wondered. Openings in her field were so few and far between. For hours at a stretch at her desk, she busied herself reviewing the existing literature on her topic; there were tons of papers but few that gave first-hand descriptions of loneliness on the spectrum. She examined the wording of these descriptions, how they voiced interpersonal relationships and the individual's place in society. The ages and backgrounds of the study participants. Whether or not each description followed a researcher's question. Which different factors were positively and negatively associated with feeling lonely.

In general, attempts to conform to neurotypical social behaviours led to increases in loneliness among autistic men and women, Kana's analysis would go on to find. It emerged that trying to mask their autism failed to alleviate the subjects' sense of not belonging. A far more effective strategy, her analysis suggested, was to encourage autistic self-esteem while building connections based on shared interests.

Once a week, Kana went to see Laura, her supervisor, to go over the progress of her research.

'How are you finding everything?' Laura asked after one of

their meetings. 'Are you fitting in okay?' Laura was in her thirties, married with young children.

Kana looked down at her fingers and gave a shy nod.

She usually spent her downtime having tea and a breather in the Centre's communal room. It was rather drab and poky. A sink and kettle and cups, plus a few chairs huddled together. On the whiteboard somebody had drawn the current research topics being explored. A man sitting with his head in his hands illustrated Kana's. The man in the drawing could have been Kana herself some days before her life overseas, ever despairing at feeling like a foreigner in her native land and language. Those days at school when she spent an eternity learning to get the hang of *kanji*, feeling lost in the dense forest of the characters' lines and dashes. Or other days when she couldn't quite get what a teacher or classmate meant to say, and no empathy came for the confusion in her that their ambiguous words had created. Or still other days when she might look into someone's eyes and not drop her gaze to their chin or neck as politeness dictated.

One spring lunchtime, as she sat on a garden bench with her sandwich, out of nowhere a gust showered Kana with cherry blossoms. In that instant she felt a sharp pang and knew that she was once again lonely. A 'force 5' loneliness, at least, because it hurt. She was homesick for her mom and her elderly sausage dog Sky. No amount of daily calls home, texts and video messages, could replace them. Homesick, too, for the friend she had left behind in Boston. Why did London have to be so far from Japan and Boston?

For a while she managed to keep it together, though the ache did not once let up. The construction work beside the Centre drilled into her nerves, and when she sat in her office the computer glared at her until she screwed up her eyes. (In her documents, she even switched the background colour from white to a soothing pale pink). By the autumn, she could tire just stepping from her lodgings to the Centre, the building's yellow bricks struck her now as jaundiced and neither did she care for the ironwork. Inside, the maze of stairs grew more bewildering, and annoying, with each passing day. Finally, at the start of winter, she had a conversation with Laura. All the courage, curiosity and sheer single-mindedness that had brought her to Britain had slowly drained out of her. Laura understood. Reluctantly Kana left to continue her research from Japan.

That was in January 2020. The country was reporting its first case of pneumonia caused by a new coronavirus from China.

Two months later the world entered lockdown.

Kana had hoped to become a full-time researcher in psychology, or possibly, a clinical counsellor – self-employed, ideally – and in the autumn of 2021, as she and her mother packed up their lives, she still did. But first, she had to wrap up her thesis; she'd do that in Okinawa now.

Bagel eaten, tea drunk, teeth and hair brushed, she returned to her room to perform some ballet stretches in front of the mirror. Still good for time before her day began. Levi knew to wait for her walk.

How much she aspired to resemble at all times this Kana in the mirror, who seemed so elegant in her gestures and in all her steps so sure-footed.

She stared up at the electronic clock display on her desk as she arched her back one last time and touched her toes. Wait two more minutes and the time will show prime numbers: 07.57,

07.58, 07.59. Now. She came out of her stretch, fetched the dog lead and walked her puppy out into the street.

This time next week, she said inwardly, she, her mom and Levi would be in Okinawa. She gazed up at the many telephone wires as they crisscrossed the horizon.

In the boxes destined for Okinawa not one item came from Kana's year in Tokyo. As the day of the move approached she had thrown out all her notes and planners and diaries from the period. Anything dated 2012. If she never read that date again, it would be too soon for her.

She'd got into Tsuda University straight out of high school, unprepared for the homesickness that awaited her in the capital. She felt out of place, unable to find her feet among the other students. There were none of the stones that she used to pick up and press into her palm on the way home from class. Her mind filled with the azalea bushes of her childhood. She wrote to her mom that she missed buying the groceries together, her walks with Sky, laying the table. Little things like that. Tokyo was too crowded and heaving. Frenetic streets and blank faces everywhere, and in these crowds she felt lonelier than ever. On campus she could go for days without exchanging a word with anyone. 'I don't know what I'm doing here,' Hiromi read. 'Nobody else seems to know either.'

The one good thing about her department – International Relations – was studying a foreign language. Changing languages – alphabet and all – made Kana feel like a new person, or perhaps simply closer to who she was inside. She was one of a handful of students who attended the Russian classes at Tsuda. She loved reading in Cyrillic, in particular a folk tale called 'The Enormous Turnip', anticipating the rhyme that capped each sentence, picturing the mouse (*myshku*) pulling the cat (*koshku*) pulling the girl (*vnuchku*) pulling the gran (*babku*) pulling the old man (*dedku*) pulling the turnip (*repku*) – 'and they pulled it out!'

'But the class I like best is English,' she said to Ms Oka, who worked in the university's counselling service. This lady was about her mother's age, she guessed, with a friendly round face. Kana had reached the point where it was either see Ms Oka or quit university. 'I've always been good at English, you see. Even though, more than Russian, you can't always be sure how to pronounce what you read. That's where my trusty old dictionary comes in. It spells out each word phonetically in an international alphabet.'

Why was she telling Ms Oka all this?

Ms Oka said, 'That's very interesting, Kana. Did you want to talk to me about anything else?'

It was just the two of them in the narrow room, their chairs opposite one another. Kana took her bag and retrieved a book. Not her dictionary, her diary.

'It'd take too long to get into why I'm here, so I brought you this.'

It felt wonderful to finally open up to somebody in her mother's absence.

Ms Oka asked if she was sure about this, handing over her diary, and she said yes – everything she wanted to talk about was in there.

They met once or twice a week after that, in the same room at the same time. Talking like this with someone, and being listened to, Kana began to understand what she was experiencing. It wasn't only homesickness. Homesickness she could manage.

This was something far stronger – loneliness unlike any she'd ever known. (Years later, putting on her researcher's hat, she could say that it had been nearly off the scale.) She felt invisible. Only Ms Oka could see and hear her.

Ms Oka could see that she was losing weight. In her lowest moments she had no energy to cook and put a meal together. She lived on rice, quick and cheap and easy to make. For days, weeks, on end she ate nothing else.

'Oka-sensei, what do you suggest I do?'

She suggested that Kana invite her mother to Tokyo.

When Hiromi saw her daughter, all forty kilos of her (thirty-eight and a half, to believe the bathroom scales, and every single gram of them weighing on her), she saw the extent of Kana's struggles. The student had lost all the vigour gained from her mother's cooking.

'I didn't want you to worry,' Kana said.

They had to find a doctor, a psychiatrist, and consult him. Hiromi wouldn't hear of taking her bullet train home before they did. It was evident that her daughter was in much distress. They went to one of those big glassy modern medical centres they have in Tokyo, where a pot-bellied man in a starched suit and tie bowed as they came in and sat around his desk. He had dyed black hair and eyes enlarged by metal-rimmed spectacles. 'What brings you here?' he asked Hiromi.

'It's my daughter,' Hiromi said. 'To be honest, Kana's always been different, ever since she was an infant. Always walking around on tiptoes.'

Kana watched her lap as the psychiatrist listened to Hiromi, averting her eyes from the certificates that covered his walls.

From time to time, she ran a hand under the lip of the imposing desk.

'I started noticing it more when she started elementary school. The scenes at the school gate when I dropped her there for class. The slightest touch from the teacher was like an electric shock.'

The memory came hurtling back to Kana; she heard her six-year-old voice repeating 'no', yelling at the top of her lungs, felt herself writhing in the grasp of the woman who was not her mother.

'Then there was the moment every afternoon when she came home from school. "How was your day?" I'd ask, and she'd give a minute-by-minute report of each of her lessons. No detail was too small. And, another thing, she referred to everyone in the class as her "friend" as if she didn't entirely understand what a "friend" is. If a teacher happened to call her Kana-chan, the teacher became her "friend" as well. It took a long time to get her to say simply "classmate". Truth is, it's never been easy for her to make friends.'

Hiromi broke off and glanced at her daughter to see if she was blushing too.

It was true, everything that her mother was saying. But that did not mean she had always felt alone. Sometimes, it had been enough to aim her thoughts elsewhere, on the pleasing shape of a stone or a phonetic symbol, and that had protected her. She'd give no thought then to the siblings other single kids often longed to play with, nor imagine, later on, taking up the life of a doting wife, a young mother, as did many teenage girls.

'Please continue,' the pot-bellied man said in a tired voice.

'If I think about it, it's not just the word "friend". Sometimes she won't say *watashi*, "I" or "me". We'll be out for a walk together in the evening and I'll say something like, "Let's start back for the apartment, I'm feeling chilly," and she'll say, "Kana, too" instead of "me, too".'

'Uh-huh,' said the man.

'It's like she speaks her own Japanese. Like she doesn't always understand other people's.' And Hiromi told him about the time she and a teenage Kana had been in town and she'd needed to dash off on an errand. 'Wait for me outside this store, and don't wander off,' she remembered saying to Kana. 'Here,' she pointed. 'I'll meet you right here in half an hour.'

'Well, then, not ten minutes after I leave, what do you know, the heavens open. And what does Kana do? She just stands there on the pavement, waiting for me outside in the pouring rain. Twenty minutes out in the pouring rain. "Why didn't you go inside the store and wait for me there?" I said to her when I got back. You should have seen her. Drenched through and through.'

'You said, wait for me outside the store,' Hiromi remembered Kana replying.

The young woman sat motionless, her head down. She kept her gaze on her lap to camouflage the frustration that was building inside her. Nothing would come of all this talk, she realised, not with this man. They should not have come here.

There was nothing wrong with her daughter's brains, Hiromi added. 'But since she began at Tsuda she's been texting all these messages home saying how unhappy she is. And when I come here, I discover she's lost 10 kilos. Too sad and stressed to eat, she says. I haven't the faintest idea what to do.'

When Hiromi finished speaking, the psychiatrist cleared his throat and projected an annoyingly know-all expression.

'I've seen cases similar to your daughter's,' he announced. 'A form of depression that we find in young, intense, educated women who push themselves too hard. These women tend to suffer from an anxiety disorder whose precise origins and nature are unclear.'

Finally, Kana looked up at the man sitting in front of his certificates. As he spoke it seemed that he was making less a confession of helplessness than asserting a status quo of medical incuriosity, which was self-explanatory and absolute.

'We can reduce your daughter's symptoms with medication. Antidepressants. I'll write a prescription now.'

The psychiatrist didn't ask Kana how she saw her future. He would not have known what to tell her, to comfort or to reassure her. She would have talked around his question. *You don't see or hear, you don't understand*, Kana imagined herself retorting. *The words depression and disorder do no justice to the person in front of you.*

'Here you are,' he said, handing the prescription to Hiromi. As he led the women to the door, Kana thought she heard him give an impatient sigh: Those silly, female, anxiety-prone nerves.

A waste of time and money, it seemed to Kana. As if she needed another person to misunderstand her. What her future wellness depended on could not be found in any pill. But at least her mother had been reassured enough to take her train home the following week.

And, not long after this disappointment, Kana began gradually to recover herself. All the time spent with her mother in Tokyo, and the regular sessions with Ms Oka, were having their effect. She felt sure that she had seen the last of doctors like the pot-bellied man. (Janine, the perceptive psychologist she'd see in Boston, would be the one finally to put autism's name to her difference.) She was coming to a momentous decision, inspired by an incipient self-confidence she owed for now to Ms Oka.

'Oka-sensei, can I ask, how did you become a clinical counsellor?'

She almost wanted to say, 'How did you become you?'

'I studied in America.'

This was what Kana heard. Her counsellor said much more, by way of detail and explanation, but it was this word, America, that grasped her imagination and would not let go.

America! And so before long it was decided, and Kana went about switching course and country.

When Kana got back from walking the puppy she went to her computer and set to her research. This time next week, she told herself again, without finishing the thought. For a time she was able to work with total concentration, her fingers typing and her feet tapping to the ballet music that filled the room. And then she found herself remembering something the British author had said to her.

Her life was a story. The writer, Danieru – Daniel – had told her this in his emails. If she wished (and how much she did wish) for it to be told, he would find the words. The story would be Kana Grace's; he would be her pen. And she thought now about her dream of the night before, and breakfast with her mom, and each of her daily routines, as if she were already telling him all about them.

Kana was nearly finished packing. The feel of gauze, cotton and soft leather alternated on her fingers. One of the boxes held nothing but her leotards, tights, costumes and *pointe* shoes – many long unwearable. But there was never any question of her letting go of them; from the tiniest up, each item was a witness to her younger selves and to her progression as a dancer.

During Kana's terrible bout of loneliness in Tokyo, what had helped to keep her sane – besides the foreign language classes and Ms Oka's counselling – was ballet. By chance, a new studio had opened its doors just across the road from her lodgings. It was minuscule. Below street level. She loved it. Several times a week after class she donned tights and soft shoes and limbered up at the horizontal bar. The first time that the instructor asked her to dance she worried she might trip over herself from being rusty, but as soon as the emphatic music began her honed legs and arms remembered every gesture, and provided each with a fluid grace, effortlessly bending and swaying.

She had attended ballet lessons since she was a small girl, to the accompaniment of a thunderous piano, in the after-school clubs that were numerous in her home town. Week after week, she worked on her insteps, learned to have a good turnout, pirouetted and practised her *entrechat*. Accepting several roles in school productions, she had been a soldier in *The Nutcracker*; another year, a snowflake.

Alongside balance and coordination, ballet helped Kana acquire the concept of personal space. The tutu was a tangible illustration, a colourful decoration, of the boundary that surrounded every dancer.

And ballet accompanied her overseas, so that wherever she would go to study, and later to perform her research, she also danced. The Boston Ballet School. The Place in London.

All through the pandemic, in her room, she had carried on her practice. And watched videos of the Royal Ballet's past productions of *The Nutcracker*, her mind spinning and leaping as she watched those graceful young women together on stage – three, six, nine . . . eighteen dancers. So nimble their every movement, so confident their identical steps, no brush of a leg or jolt of an arm outstretched, no collision. Eighteen personal spaces dancing in parallel, in harmony, separately and yet as one.

Her travels had broadened Kana's mind immeasurably. And from the time she had returned to the mainland, Kana knew that she would once more leave. And take her mom and dog with her. The inhabitants of mainland Japan were among the loneliest on earth. You had only to follow the media in recent years to think so. Hardly a week or month passed now without Kana and Hiromi reading or watching or hearing some report about the *hikikomori*, the adult recluses holed up in a bedroom of their ageing parents' home; or about a forgotten elderly neighbour who had been left to wizen into a mummy; or about the men and women who drop everything to run off and go missing, joining the tens of thousands each year who become *jouhatsu*, 'evaporated people'.

Not once did Kana consider these reports to be mere sensationalism or purely anecdotal. She knew families in which a grandfather or some other relative had 'evaporated' long ago just like the reporters said. She could not help but wonder if loneliness ran in many Japanese families.

But with Hiromi, to whom she had always been so close, and could speak her mind, never having to stand on ceremony,

Kana found it nearly impossible to discuss *kodoku*, loneliness. Her mom, she knew, had to feel lonely sometimes. When does that happen? She would have liked to ask her mom, but never dared. How long does the feeling last? What makes it better or worse? These were questions she was always asking in her research. Another was, what words would you use to describe your loneliness?

Mother and daughter were sharing one of their last suppers in Utsunomiya when Kana asked this question under cover of a word game. She was thinking of a certain category of words in Japanese, onomatopoeic, that evoke sensations and states of mind. *Kura kura*, for example, a sound associated with giddiness; *zuki zuki*, with painful throbbing.

Kana put down her chopsticks and said, 'When I think of feeling lonely, I think of the word *buru buru*. It sounds just like the feeling, don't you think?'

'*Buru buru*?' Hiromi had finished her gyoza dumpling. 'Yes, I suppose. Yes, I can see that.'

The sound usually described someone trembling – trembling from the cold or fright.

'Like not having the warmth of someone close to you,' Hiromi pursued. 'Or feeling afraid on account of being on your own.'

'Yes, exactly.' And seeing her chance, Kana went on, 'And with what sound do you associate feeling lonely?'

Hiromi's face turned thoughtful.

'*Chiku chiku*,' she said at last.

It was a sound used to refer to a prickling pain.

Was it precisely this pain, *chiku chiku*, that her mother had felt during Kana's years abroad?

This photo album had travelled with her all the way from Boston. Of course it was going to Okinawa. It was a repurposed scrapbook filled with snapshots of Kana's time in America, decorated with origami and bright pink stickers. Some days Kana would pull out the album and look over the pictures. There she was sitting on the manicured lawn at a students' picnic. And there she was with her friend Kara, sharing a couch and coffee. And there was Kara saying something to the camera. And there they were in a head shot, beaming.

The album had been Kara's parting gift to her – the work of several thoughtful hours.

Kara Rodano was the best friend that Kana had always dreamed of having, the kind of friend she hadn't been quite certain even existed outside of movies, novels and pop songs. She had met her on campus, in an aerobics group, after which they had begun spending time getting to know one another. Kara was from Fallston, Maryland. She was studying communication science and planned to become a speech-language pathologist. She shared Kana's interest in the mind and helping others, and though she wasn't the best cook in the world, not by a long shot, when it came to baking she sure knew her way around an oven.

Americans were fascinating to Kana, ever since her three-week homestay in Indiana. That had been right at the beginning, before Boston, when her body clock was still on Japanese time. She'd remembered to stand at the right distance from her hosts, allowing for the imaginary tutus around their waists as they talked and walked and went sightseeing. Kana was charmed by the Americans' voluble hospitality; the regular potlucks to which she would contribute a salad; their habit of making quote marks with their fingers as they spoke.

But it was with Kara that she would acquire a rapport. That was something new for Kana, and magical. The two young women, hanging out, could talk for hours and neither of them notice the time. Rapidly Kana's soft voice matched Kara's accent – she pronounced Maryland as 'Marilyn' and said 'jeet yet?' for 'did you eat yet?' like a Marylander born and bred. Without trying, at least too consciously, she held herself like Kara – or, rather, like Kara in front of Kana. The same straight back, the same folded hands, the same intent gaze. Sitting and talking face to face, they looked like mirror images of one another.

In the album a close-up photo showed the two friends in an excited hug. It captured the day Kana had become certain that their bond was something special. They were sitting on the dorm couch, in the middle of one of the 'deep conversations' they enjoyed.

'No way,' said Kara. 'Seriously, you don't know your personality type?'

'Seriously,' Kana said.

Kara got up a web page on her phone. It was a five-minute, multiple-choice quiz, of the kind that appear in waiting-room magazines. Kana took the phone and responded to the questions, agreeing or disagreeing with a list of statements. When Kara was shown the result she squealed with joy.

They had the exact same personality type.

Now, it was simply a quiz, a thought-provoking bit of fun, and Kana knew better than to treat the result too seriously. Yet her having responded just like Kara, even more than the result pronouncing them both intuitive, diligent and compassionate introverts, pleased her no end.

Kara smiled wide at Kana and Kana smiled wide at Kara. Their mutual excitement confirmed to each that their feelings were reciprocated. When Kana saw herself in her friend's gaze, she saw the assured and cheerful woman she'd hoped she might one day become. She no longer felt her difference as a burden, weighing her down into solitude.

After Kana returned to Japan, the friends would use every way at their disposal to stay connected: letters and parcels, calls and email, text and video messages. Also: prayers.

Kana, on her plane from America, had carried a Bible.

'You're a Christian?' Hiromi repeated the word with unconcealed confusion. Their spirituality had been limited to dropping coins in the local shrine's collection box on New Year's Day.

'Kurisuchan?' Hiromi said again inwardly, but no, the word still meant very little to her. Adam and Eve, Noah's Ark – that was more or less it.

In time Kana would answer her mom's questions about Jesus and the Gospels. She would attempt to describe what she experienced when she prayed to God and felt His shining presence – felt it all the more keenly when she was alone. Like a light. No, more than that. Like moonlight beaming through the dark. For now, she showed her the Bible that Kara had shown Kana in Boston, and said more or less what her friend had said.

This here, Kara had said, shyly producing the book from a drawer, wasn't any old book. She meant, it was a book of course, with pages and everything, and old, thousands of years old in fact, but what she was saying was, it told a story unlike any other. One big story through many smaller ones, some so small blink once, twice and you'd miss them, too small for other books, but included between these covers, even the tiniest, lowliest lives, because you could not tell the one big story without them, every single one, they were all woven together.

'You know,' Kara had said, 'it's so hard to talk about the deep stuff. Like love.'

Her voice had changed when she said 'love'.

'And like what makes each of us, us. Super hard for everyone. Words don't seem up to it. But this,' and Kana now patted the book on the table before her mom, 'this gives us the words to ponder. At least, I believe so.'

Okinawa. Even in November the air was several degrees warmer than on the mainland. Beyond Hiromi and Kana's new apartment palm trees threw their spiky shade onto the footpaths, and the sandy beach stretched out forever. Flags drowsed on their poles when the weather was calm and the musical drawl of the locals carried far and wide.

The move, like most house moves, had been tense and draining. But each of the boxes had landed on the island, and then reached Chatan, beside the American Village, in one piece. Kana's Bible and photo album and ballet clothes and research folders promptly made themselves at home, divvying up between them the best spots around the bare shelves and drawers and wardrobe.

Not long afterwards, Kana heard that her research on loneliness was going to appear in a scientific journal in the spring. She spent sunny weeks walking Levi by the sea as she imagined other researchers discovering her work in print. Who knew to where their comments and feedback might yet take her thoughts? Her good mood during this time made her unusually forthcoming. One afternoon, as she was queueing for the vet, an American-sounding voice asked her in English, what was her cute-looking dog's name? She turned and saw a blonde woman's tan and smile and answered. Dogs were a safe, reliable way to open a conversation anywhere. On top of that, Kana always felt so much more confident when she could speak in English. She asked for and was given the name of the American woman's poodle. By the looks of things, Levi and the poodle were already firm friends. Their owners stood and chatted until it was Kana's turn to go in.

'See you around,' said the poodle's owner.

When the journal article appeared, Kana emailed Kara at once to let her know. Then she emailed the British writer, who replied with congratulations and the news that his narrative about her was almost there. He just needed to study up a bit on Okinawa.

For centuries the Okinawans traded with the mainland, China and other lands in East and South East Asia. Even as Japan isolated itself from the world, goods and peoples and traditions continued to meet and mix on the annexed island. The Shoguns neglected the islanders, world war devastated them, but their culture of welcome and inclusion survived. The Okinawans are easy-going; their lives are slower than those on the mainland, more relaxed, and very long. They have a one-word philosophy: *yuimaru*. It isn't a Japanese word, it is Okinawa dialect for 'looking out for one another'. A newcomer to the island will be asked, more than once, if any help is required. An islander not seen for a day or two will be checked on. And at the approach of a typhoon, the Okinawans do more than batten down the hatches. They share their homes and food with neighbours as everyone waits for the storm to pass.

Warren

For a long time now, he'd had no life worthy of the name. Then, on the morning of 28 November 2012, he'd been found face down in the lake in Dartmouth Park, West Bromwich – by a passer-by according to one local report, by park rangers according to another – with his throat slit, his escaping blood leaving meaningless squiggles upon the water's surface.

Almost as soon as he'd been found, however, the dead man had been forgotten. Other than the circumstances of his death he had no claim on people's attention. For reporters there were always more glamorous murders to cover, better-looking victims whose photos, in death as in life, caught the eye and touched a nerve, whose sticky ends generated the clicks and the buzz that paid their salaries. For most residents of the town he'd been only a stranger, no one special, though quite a few among them would have seen him on the streets where he'd crawled the pubs and slept rough some nights, more so in his final months. He'd had no wife turned widow to keep his memory alive, no close friends left behind to mourn. No money for the kind of showy funeral that reliably draws a crowd. So, in the end, just as if the dead man had never lived there, or indeed had never lived at all, the town went on as before and soon forgot him.

Detective Inspector Warren Hines had not, though, and never would. Through all the months of his inquiry, Warren had got to know the dead man well, better it might be said than those who had known him alive. From time to time, as the years went on, he would continue to think of the man, as he did now in 2022, with the hindsight of the intervening decade, during which a lasting bout of depression had resulted in his being diagnosed, at age fifty, on the autistic spectrum. Perhaps it had taken someone like him, Warren found himself thinking, someone with his cast of mind to get to the bottom of such a baffling and curious case.

From an article in the *Express and Star*, dated 28 November 2012:

A body was discovered floating in the boating lake of a West Bromwich park today, sparking a police investigation.

West Midlands Police spokeswoman Deb Edmonds said: 'We are treating the death as unexplained at the moment and we are asking anyone with information to contact police.'

Annette Welch, secretary of Friends of Dartmouth Park, said that she was shocked to hear what had happened.

'I can't believe it,' she said. 'I was only walking by the lake around 9 a.m. this morning and I thought it was unusually busy.'

One 73-year-old man, who visits the park twice a day with his dogs, but wished to remain anonymous, said: 'The first I heard about it was when I saw the police down here this morning. We don't know what could have happened.

I know people do drink in the park. It's possible someone could have come down here last night and fallen in.'

Warren was quick to the scene that morning, brought there by his trusty Mini. A well-worn brown trilby and woollen scarf kept away the water's icy breath. The lake was home to some Canada geese who honked as they were cordoned off, while, held back around its banks, men and women gathered for the impromptu spectacle. Then, one by one, losing interest, they peeled away.

The dead man had been fished out and driven away to the morgue for a post-mortem. Of South Asian heritage, between forty and forty-five years old, short dark hair, brown eyes, slender, average height. Gazing round at its scruffy trees and barren grass, Warren thought about how the park must have withheld hospitality from the man in his final moments. He was familiar enough with the site to know what he wasn't looking at. The Refreshment Room (burned down by vandals in the eighties); the boathouse (burned down by vandals – the same or others – in the nineties); the art deco bandstand (demolished after rust devoured its walls). The presently non-existent benches you could not sit or lie down on. What on earth, then, had impelled the man to be out here in the smallest hours of a midweek morning? In the biting cold and dank and dark. A lovers' tryst? A drug deal? An insomniac's desperate urge to stretch his legs? For now, every scenario was possible.

Including suicide. That couldn't be ruled out, not right away. There was the stubborn argument of statistics – most of the time a violent death's victim and perpetrator bear one and the same name – but equally the setting of this man's demise, once body and identity were reunited, seemed to corroborate the idea of a truly desperate act.

The man's name, the police learned, was Jasbir Singh Bains. Forty-one and of no fixed abode. That might explain what he was doing out in the middle of the night, having no indoors to leave. A local man – you couldn't get more local – from Herbert Street, where he'd grown up, it was no more than a ten-minute walk to the lake. Acquaintances described a harmless drifter, long down on his luck, who'd let the years slip by and drunk whatever money came his way, living as if there were no tomorrow.

It wasn't implausible, then, that he would have taken a knife to his own throat and ended his life, after wandering through the dark into a final ambush of desperation. Perhaps he'd chosen this desolate spot to die because it reminded him of his childhood, of racing in and out of the shadows of trees, of family picnics on the grass after which he'd fed breadcrumbs to the lake.

Some of Warren's youngest colleagues protested. A bloke slash his own throat? They were newbies and Warren gave them a look he reserved for people who talked daft. The kind who thought they'd seen it all. No one ever had. You couldn't begin to understand the harm a human being might inflict on another, Warren said, until you saw what harm they were all capable of inflicting upon themselves. He told them about the time his squad had attended an address in Sandwell. Reports of a domestic dispute earlier in the week. Neighbours hadn't seen the young woman since. Warren watched his team knock and knock before they took down the front door; he heard a gasp escape them when they went in. They'd entered the woman's living room, and turned away instinctively at the sight of so much blood. Blood on the carpet and on the bare wall and on the kitchen knife that lay beside her – the knife that had stabbed her chest over and over again. Everyone thought murder, even Warren, until he studied more closely the steady, rhythmic pattern in the bloodstains. He saw then what must have happened: the shouts of recrimination, words that could not be unheard, the boyfriend storming out, the woman's violent weeping. A broken heart. Thoughts that cloud and darken. Difficulty breathing – and too much pain. The shudder of cutlery in the drawer jolted open. Her body leaning still against the wall before each releasing thrust of the blade.

The woman whom neighbours spoke of as gentle and level-headed.

But in this case that explanation – suicide – didn't hold up. Having inspected the lake, police divers returned to Warren and his team empty-handed. A body with a slit throat found, but no knife – or other sharp instrument – had been recovered. That, together with the way the blood had fanned upon the water, told Warren the victim had been surprised. He hadn't been at the water's edge alone.

For a murderer the park had several advantages. The absence of street lights and surveillance gave freedom of movement to nocturnal visitors; tall trees and boarded-up fences conspired to screen them from the gazes of the outside world. There were multiple entrances and exits, where the killer could have slipped away – one on Herbert Street and Beeches Road, also on Lodge Hill, and another, to the north, on Dagger Lane.

In his previous life Warren had fixed cars. His father was in the motor trade and had apprenticed him at sixteen, thinking, the lad had never fitted in at school. The suburb of Hall Green in the seventies wasn't the easiest place for the odd and shy to stick out – even someone like Warren, who had a good head on his shoulders. He hated the playing fields – footie and the like – hated being jostled. Whistles, claps and pops rumpled his brow and hurt his ears. He puzzled over the conversations he heard, the turns of phrase, the words that might mean one thing or something else altogether. What was that about? His puzzlement got the better of him and he steered clear of his classmates' games and maintained a cautious distance. He always had the feeling someone was trying to have him over.

The worst of it were the bullying fists and the insults he always took without a fight. He warded them off with his absence; teachers counted his distress in days off sick. Moving comprehensives didn't help, only growing up did.

When Warren joined the police at the end of his twenties, keen to work more with his mind, he brought to it, besides a desire to catch the adult world's bullies, his long experience of cars. Solving injustices was something like repairing cars. A small voice on the phone would report an offence and it'd be like being back at the garage in Digbeth, someone trailing in a Morris Minor that wouldn't start or a misfiring Ford Escort and nothing else for it but to flip the bonnet and get stuck into the engine, get his hands mucky, track the source of the trouble methodically to some broken part or dingy corner.

With his mind, as before with his hands, he groped his way towards solutions. He familiarised himself with each crime's make and model and analysed its inner workings. A premeditated act required a certain amount of planning to run smoothly:

how to get from A to B, what to wear, where to dispose of a weapon. The nuts and bolts.

The mechanics of a crime, of a murder, were something you could take apart and reconstruct, if you knew how.

His higher-ups liked him; he was meticulous, the way he worked through a case, taking his thinking home and returning from the weekend with possible solutions or some penetrating insight. Working all hours, he wasn't the least bit put out. He was a man of simple pleasures. Also of strong tastes – curry, the spiciest ones, and coarse pipe tobacco – because he had hardly any sense of smell, which came in handy when you crossed as many dead bodies as he did.

Even as he climbed the ranks he abstained from office politics, making neither friends nor foes among his colleagues. He'd respond to their 'Guv?' with only a brief request they were quick to fulfil. They brought him witness statements to reread, crime scene photos to pore over from another angle; watched his pipe disappear inside his jacket as he rose to leave for an interrogation. Later they could see him outside, heading for his car, his pipe sending up pensive rings of blue smoke.

'Trilby's on the case,' the policemen said to one another, alluding to the brown hat worn by Warren indoors and out, in all weathers. It was a rare day when you saw the detective without his trilby. The snug, narrow-brimmed hat shielded his senses from all manner of glints and creaks and hums: it helped him to think.

Jasbir Singh Bains had been murdered. But murders came in a range of models. Warren and his team dealt with hate crimes and honour killings and eliminations of a rival or of a witness, lethal bust-ups – and these were just for starters. Deaths motivated by envy, vengeance, frustrated lust, and greed – the list went on. Which had driven Jasbir's killer? Warren asked himself. A model that featured a particular focus on location and timing, swift and calculated. A focus greater than, say, a hate crime usually had; far greater than a bust-up. It resembled more a killing for greed's sake, which were common enough. Greed iced pity, chloroformed a conscience, stiffened the will to act.

But other than a modest mobile phone, which had vanished, and the £22 found on him, the dead man had possessed nothing, it seemed, for an aggressor to steal.

Balwinder Singh, Jasbir's cousin and employer, reported being the last person to have seen him alive. The cousins had grown up together, and lately Jasbir had been working as a machinist in Balwinder's firm.

'They are going to kill me,' Balwinder said.

This was what Jasbir had told his cousin on the evening of the murder, the two men alone and Balwinder trying to settle him down for the night. Jasbir was between temporary accommodations.

Balwinder had given him twenty quid and put him up in a room above the Desi Junction pub on the High Street. Jasbir veered between exhaustion and agitation; he was rambling.

'About what?' Warren asked.

'Something about a young woman. A woman he'd met and made pregnant. The people around her were mad angry.'

Jasbir was afraid for his life. People were after him.

Who this woman or the other people might be Balwinder hadn't a clue – Jasbir hadn't made a whole lot of sense that evening.

Had the cousin, by any chance, heard him say anything about a meeting in the park, or anywhere else, later that night? No, nothing about any meeting.

'I'm going to go to sleep,' had been Jasbir's last words, as though to assuage his cousin's concern. 'I'm not going to come out now.' Balwinder had answered that he was right to get his head down; he was expecting him in for work in the morning.

The cousin had left him before closing time.

I'd imagined him for years before I met the detective. Quite unawares, I'd been in search of him for the story I vaguely hoped one day to write: a story of murderous mystery solved by a neurodivergent policeman. I trusted such a person really did exist.

Like many autistic boys – like young Warren, too, as I would learn – following the adventures of one particular famous detective consumed a fair bit of my adolescence. Sherlock Holmes appeared in a variety of forms: in the much-borrowed library books, as well as their adaptation for TV – films and episodes broadcast on lazy weekends and endlessly replayed. I remember the audacious chases, and the smoggy cobbled streets and Jeremy Brett frowning through a magnifying glass as he reasoned his way to the right suspect.

Warren had the pipe and the headwear but he wasn't acting a part, nor was he the figment of any author's creation. He had been in the force for over twenty years when I learned of him.

He had made public appeals in connection with his cases, and more recently given an interview in the regional press. From Paris, where I lived, I accessed this online article about his life and career. It had appeared in the *Birmingham Mail* three years earlier. The headline said, 'Meet the autistic Birmingham murder detective: "I see things differently to everyone else."'

At the time of his interview Warren had not long received his diagnosis, and when I got in touch with him, in mid-2021, it was something he was still working through. He had a hard time answering some of my questions; they awakened memories that could be painful. He was far more used to doing the asking than the answering. And then the long stifling summer came – both to Paris and Warren's rural village in North Warwickshire – and almost shut down our conversation for good. It was the summer Warren's father was taken to a hospice and his horse Tom – Tom A Hawk – died. There were worse things for a horse (or a father) than dying of old age but that didn't make Warren's sorrow any less acute. He had grown up close to stables, near where his parents' friends owned a farm, and learned to ride saddleless. The instant bond he'd made with the horses had been magical, the connection with another sentient being who would never judge him and with whom the line of communication was always open. Many happy hours of rhythmic trotting jogged his growing brain and exercised his alertness. As an adult, riding Tom A Hawk at the weekend kept him on an even keel.

'My father and my horse were the closest friends I had,' Warren wrote to me in a brief and reflective email. He hoped to pursue our exchanges 'once some of the emptiness has passed'. My heart went out to him, and the writing could wait. I wanted to give him all the time and peace that he might need. But through the wet weeks of early autumn, the colder and shrinking days that were only going to get gloomier, it seemed to me that Warren's mood might never lift. Perhaps our aborted correspondence had been irremediably tainted by grief.

The weeks of waiting turned to months and autumn to winter. And to top it all off, the Omicron virus cancelled Christmas. In the New Year I contemplated dropping the story. I regretted not happening on Warren's interview in the press earlier.

Then, just before the spring, our conversation resumed and we swapped emails and video-called over several days. Warren had rallied since adopting a bay gelding he named Rolo. He was self-effacing as ever, preferring to concentrate our exchanges on the victims of homicides he'd helped to solve (and whose every name he could still recall), but he spoke as well about his childhood and his family, about how he got into policing, about the ways in which he and his colleagues thought very differently.

'Sometimes they'll tell themselves a story,' he said. 'They don't mean to, but they'll convince themselves that the person they think is guilty really is. Because this suspect was in the vicinity of the crime at the hour in question and has form but no alibi.'

Colleagues would fall in with each other's certainty, Warren said. 'Everything seems to fit, everything points to so-and-so. Some can get pretty wound up if you can't see how everything points to so-and-so. The CCTV. So-and-so is all over it. Take a look for yourself.'

So Warren would take a look, but something would niggle at him. A problem of logic. The guy takes the scenic route from a crime scene, in the full glare of CCTV? He's much street-wiser than that. And sure enough, after some further inquiries, so-and-so would prove not to be their man.

'I suppose I don't jump to conclusions. I inch towards them. I'm wary of obvious. Obvious isn't always right.'

We discussed murder in fiction – what TV and novels got right and wrong about it. I was thinking of the story – Warren's story – I intended to write. I didn't want to make the mistakes he could at least warn me of.

'Behind every detective there's a whole team knocking on doors, chasing up possible leads. Boring leg work, but it's essential. Without it the detective is nothing. Other than helping with that I'd spend a lot of my time at a desk, mulling a case. Think a middle-aged bloke on his own in his office. Think silence. Not much of the racing about and shouting and other carrying-on you see on the box or read in some books.'

I asked him to describe his most fiendish case and he did so, though there was a limit to how much he could say. For the rest, there were old press articles and other sources of information if I knew where to look.

The Bains case.

The Man in the Lake.

A flummoxed Balwinder, the dead man's cousin, was talking to the media. He was wearing a black hooded top and a grey baseball cap which he pushed back from his unshaven face for the cameras.

'Someone must have entrapped Jasbir. I think he was in a honey trap, to be honest.'

It was 5 December, a week since the killing, and still the

police had no eyewitnesses, no firm leads, no persons of interest. The weather was good enough to hold the press conference
in the park, around the lake.

The day was clear, the sky azure, and Balwinder's eyes took
the cool sunlight without blinking. Behind him the calm lake
sparkled. You would never have known that a body had been
floating there just a few days earlier.

A picture of the dead man, alive, was distributed to the press.
Cropped black hair. A smooth, straight face, above a beige cardi-
gan. The eyes were lowered as if to avoid the viewer's gaze.

Warren appealed for anyone who had known Jasbir to come
forward. He needed to learn as much as he could about his
background, whom he associated with, what he did with his
time and where he went. A radio journalist's microphone was
recording, a TV man was filming, and a pair of reporters filled a
page of their notepads as the detective spoke.

Appeals to the general public stirred mixed feelings in
Warren. For every serious response there might be no short-
age of time wasters, unbalanced attention seekers who handed
themselves in under false pretences. It could be unnerving to
watch them re-enact their fantasy crimes, watch them give
it their all as they made an impossible firearm out of thumb,
middle finger and index; rammed would-be blades into all the
wrong places; curled their fingers and strangled the air until
they were red in the face. How crestfallen they looked when
told they were free to go.

So the prospect of being roped into their audience, of
having to sit through these people's palaver, their nonsense,
shortened a temper that, in Warren, was longer than most. But
it was all part of the job, you got used to it more or less, the
hassle quickly forgiven if the appeal helped to bring some new

detail to light. For a week now he'd felt as though he were working in the dark.

Instead of answers he was uncovering more and more questions. 'I'm appealing for anyone who knew Jasbir to come forward.' But how many had known Jasbir really?

He'd gone to the dead man's workplace and spoken with the men at their machines. Jasbir had been a good worker, they said. They'd had no complaints. He had never been heard to say a bad word about anyone.

No sharp tool had been reported missing.

He'd gone to the pubs and spoken to the regulars, showing the picture to refresh memories. The Jasbir in the picture looked rather abashed at all the attention.

He'd asked about Jasbir's demeanour on the night in question, and in the evenings leading up to it, whether he had said anything, been seen with anyone, perhaps been bought a round of drinks, but the regulars just looked up from their pints and shrugged, dunno, no, sorry, can't help you, and whatever he'd said or done no one seemed to care to recall.

The barmen, too, shook their heads and wiped their hands with their towels. He'd had a few, as usual, was their recollection. He hadn't been one for confidences.

From both sides of his family Warren had carried on something special that went back generations. His father's side had bequeathed him 'Warren' which had once been his grandmother's name, that is, her maiden name, then his father's middle name before becoming his own. On his mother's side, several relatives had been seen as eccentric and keepers of their own company, and Warren would tell me he assumed his autism had come down from them.

There was his mother's cousin, whom he'd called 'Uncle' and who had made his career as an Egyptologist. He remembered the thick bushy beard that hid half this solitary uncle's face and the tanned sinewy arms from digs in distant lands, but even more so the endless erudition as the man talked stelae and sarcophagi with his cousin's eight-year-old son. By the age of nine Warren had been taught – much to his delight – to decipher hieroglyphs.

He was thinking also of two sisters of his grandmother Williams, the grandmother who wasn't Warren, great-aunts who had dealt in antiquities and lived out in the middle of nowhere, far away in the countryside. Of these great-aunts, and his summer stays with them as a child, Warren had retained fond and vivid memories.

'Here's 50p for you,' one or another of these old sisters would say when Warren was down to his last few pence in pocket money, bending and handing him the shiny seven-sided coin whose value they still reckoned inwardly in shillings. With that coin weighting the pocket of his shorts Warren would go and buy himself a paper bagful of sweets, then wander off over the fields feeling as prosperous as must do millionaires.

He wandered to his heart's content, wandered high and low over the hilly miles, left entirely to his own devices. He could have vanished ten times over before either sister would have thought to look for him.

One of the great-aunts kept horses and lived with a pet sheep, Horace, close to the ruins of an ancient estate, its buildings long gone to seed and overgrown with thick roots and branches. It was little wonder that she preferred to walk Horace further afield, on flatter ground, occasionally stopping to give it digestive biscuits. Warren, on the other hand, loved investigating those ruins – there wasn't a nook or cranny he wouldn't visit to appease his curiosity. Halls that were shells of their former selves, a tower without any of its floors. High above him, the cawing of ravens. He stepped through gaping arched doorways, pressing a palm to the mossy stone walls as he peered out from the glassless windows. However long and often he toured these grounds he never once killed time there; always he found something to occupy his mind. Always the scattered shards of some pot or saucer to reconstruct. A date or inscription for him to piece together. A remnant of some porcelain plate he might hold up to the light and admire for many minutes – a tribute to the beauty of its floral motifs.

The other great-aunt had bought an old lodge and given it over to her collection. For tens of years she had been collecting every kind of doll that she could purchase. Hundreds of dolls crammed into every inch and corner of the downstairs rooms, but lined up and labelled along shelves and in smart display cases.

'See this one, Warren?' this great-aunt would push her thick glasses up her nose and point at one of the cases. 'Made of wax, from around 1810. A pedlar.'

Some were English, some were Continental. Others were Russian. They were all different shapes and sizes. One stood tall and leggy, another small and round; this doll had a Victorian bonnet, that doll wore a petticoat.

On a hot day their owner wore a sari. She was the older of the two sisters, born in 1915, and gave next to no thought to appearances. But she was doll house-proud.

Warren levelled his gaze at the miniature furniture – teensy chairs and tables laden with cut-out foods, microscopic cup-boards that opened on crockery and drawers on cutlery, inch-high grandfather clocks and made beds and baths and hat stands. A tiny walnut bookcase containing even tinier books containing the complete works of Shakespeare.

Only the fact that he could never play with any of these toys, could touch them with his eyes but not with his sticky fingers, lightly adulterated his pleasure. But he handled each of them firmly in his mind and, years later, whenever he imagined the solution to a crime, he wondered if what he saw – the little figures and objects set against various backdrops in his mind's eye – wasn't like some tragic scene out of his great-aunt's collection.

Warren loosened his scarf as he turned onto Salisbury Road. He walked up the path to one of the houses and when he reached the door the occupant answered and let him in. The man – he was in his early forties and bald – continued to stand expec-tantly even after Warren had stepped into the narrow hallway. Then he offered Warren tea or coffee and they sat in the front room.

The dead man's former schoolmate, Jagdev Rai, said that maybe his old friend had kept bad company, he didn't know, he had never pried into that side of his life. He and Jasbir went way back, that was correct, but even so Jasbir didn't tell him everything.

Jasbir had been over to the house several times in the past year, Rai said. To have a bath and a warm bite to eat and a proper kip. His wife and kids liked him. Everyone liked Jasbir. He was easy-going and charming. You couldn't help liking him.

Did Jasbir have a key to the house? Warren wondered. No. It was always better to be around. There was the outdoor, you know, the off-licence, a few doors away. Though the family couldn't always be at home. Jasbir would call or text in advance. In case Rai had a wedding somewhere – he was a caterer. Otherwise Jasbir would pop over of an evening and when he was tired he'd go and kip in the van. The white van parked behind the house. He preferred that to the settee. More private. And he could leave when he pleased.

Warren asked about Canada – a possible new lead turned up by his team's inquiries. Wanting to make a fresh start, the dead man had emigrated in 2006. He had some relatives in Canada. But about a year ago, towards the end of 2011, Jasbir had returned. Apparently his return to the UK was unexpected. Had he got himself in hot water over there? Might he have been running away from something, or from somebody?

Rai said he didn't know anything about that. Jasbir had never talked to him about Canada.

Of course the detective could have a look inside the van.

Warren followed Rai round the house and sighted the Mercedes-Benz Sprinter. First generation. When had Jasbir last kipped in there?

Rai thought for a moment as he unlocked the van. The twenty-sixth. November twenty-sixth. The night before Jasbir had stayed in the room above the pub, and left in the early hours for the park. The night before his last.

Where Jasbir had slept a dusty blanket lay rumpled on the passenger seat. Warren thought he could make out the faint impression left by the man whose sleep was now eternal.

✳

Warren

The present would be nothing without the past, Warren has always known. He has known it from as far back as he can remember. He is both a man of his time – and of another time, more so as he has grown older. In his social media posts, which began in 2013, photos of his horse riding – a rare way to stay in the here and now – alternate with retweets of BBC Archive clips, 'on this day' memorials, snippets of jumpy home movies featuring cars, and black-and-white photos of bygone cityscapes.

Warren is old enough to recall the thrill that was riding the 90 bus towards the suburbs of Birmingham. He'd take a top-deck seat right at the front and fidget until the approach to Camp Hill. His fellow schoolboys and the older teens, in the surrounding rows, grew equally tense and quiet. And then it appeared, in the near distance: The Camp Hill flyover. A narrow, shuddery ramp across a busy junction, prefabricated in steel and concrete. The bus would pick up speed as it climbed into the sky, your breathing went on pause, the tops of buildings blurring until they disappeared. You felt the rise and the dip in the pit of your stomach; it was like being astride a giant racehorse.

How was such an experience possible in the middle of an otherwise flat city, Warren's ever-enquiring mind wanted to learn. When had this particular section of road been erected and why? It had to have a history – a sequence of events, now invisible, which had forged what people presently saw, and it astonished him that in perceiving this he was rather unusual. The ramp spanned many metres and several decades. For children of Warren's age, and older, the Camp Hill flyover had always been there. They assumed it was a road, just a road, like any other.

Warren's father had long encouraged his son's frequent questions, his interrogating nature, and he was quick to say that Warren was right. Things are never only as they appear. Because something is doesn't mean it always was. What his classmates all viewed as a permanent fixture had once been the epitome of temporary constructions. Engineers had put it up one weekend in 1961 as a stopgap cure for traffic jams.

Perhaps they had forgotten to take it down. Perhaps they had forgotten they'd ever put it up.

It was January 2013 and the police investigation into Jasbir's death had slowed. Canada was hardly next door. By the middle of the month the West Midlands sky looked like snow. Residents took salt and shovels to the roads and pavements. The lake in the park froze and thawed and in February froze again.

The events of the evening and night of 27 to 28 November remained a mystery, every avenue of the inquiry seeming to go nowhere. Every time Warren and his team thought they were getting warmer their leads fell through. Impossible to ascertain the whereabouts of the dead man's mobile phone, or the sharp instrument that had ended his life. The police would have revisited the scenario of suicide but for the fact that no such instrument had been found at the scene.

No knife at the scene. No farewell note left anywhere either. No history of previous suicide attempts or even of depression. No hesitation marks on the dead man's throat. That Warren should mentally rehearse all these points spoke to the sombre mood in his team. If any of his overworked colleagues was thinking of moving on, who could blame them? And it was also true that, in his final months, Jasbir's position had become parlous, not to say desperate. Warren and his team were learning just how parlous from their inquiries. For years he had been borrowing money from family and friends; he was thousands of pounds in debt.

On the snowiest days Warren and his team reviewed CCTV recordings of the hours preceding Jasbir's death. Seven hundred hours of tape taken from forty-six locations around the area. It would take a person one whole month non-stop to view all the footage, two if they blinked, three if they ate and slept – so Warren's colleagues focused their attention on the time and sites closest to the incident. They watched and watched and watched the sleeping streets that circled the park, and they did not see anyone running, or even walking, away.

As for Warren, he was never out of patience and he watched one tape in particular, rewinding and pausing, rewinding a little more, then a little bit more again . . .

Our lives are lived forwards but understood backwards.

This thought, and others like it, came to Warren as he wandered in a churchyard in Bromsgrove. Certain free days, he liked nothing better than to drive over there and read the gravestones. The oldest had been weathered near illegible, but he would stop and crouch, brush away the dirt and moss and recover a name, an age, a date of death, occasionally, a brief tale – clues to a prior existence that had otherwise vanished without a trace.

On one stone he read:

TO THE MEMORY OF THOMAS SCAIFE.
Late an Engineer on the Birmingham and Gloucester Railway
who lost his life at Bromsgrove Station by the Explosion of
an Engine Boiler on Tuesday the 10th of November 1840.
He was 28 Years of Age, highly esteemed
by his fellow workmen
for his many amiable qualities, and his
Death will be long lamented
by all those who had the pleasure of his acquaintance.

. . .

THIS STONE WAS ERECTED AT THE JOINT EXPENCE
OF HIS FELLOW WORKMEN 1842

The stone was black and white and chipped and scraped in places, and Warren noticed how it must have been repainted and restored several times down the years. He was moved by the tale it told, the desire to keep alive a friend's name, and impressed that the workmen had paid out of their meagre wages, over a period of two years, to do so.

He stood before the grave for some time, his trilby lowered, before he left the yard.

The images on Warren's screen didn't seem to be the wisest use of a detective's attention. Colleagues had already looked at this residential camera footage: dingy white cement render with a small green metal gate to the right. Hours of nothing to meet the eye but this side of a house and its green gate. But Warren, rewinding, had an idea that there might be something more to see. You just had to go back far enough. He rewound the hours until, at last, he stumbled on the minute when a bow windowpane came into view. Unpeeled eyes could easily have missed that pane, as it was near the periphery of the image.

The house had moved several inches. The observant camera must have swivelled. But no gust of wind could have done that – only a human hand. Warren timed the change in angle to the start of the evening of 27 November – six or so hours before Jasbir's death.

He continued to rewind and pause and play the tape. More side wall and gate, but now with the bow windowpane on the far right side of the picture. Once in a while a neighbour's car could be seen passing the wall, in either direction, to park behind the house or to drive away. Warren was more interested in the pane. Because just beyond the pane, and the rest of the bow window, there would be the front door. So that anyone entering or leaving flashed in the corner of the camera's eye. A marginal shadow, a fraction of a second, but the movement was recorded. Unless and until, that is, someone thought to avert the camera's gaze.

The house was on Salisbury Road. Warren had rounded that same side wall and gate to inspect the Mercedes van. He returned now with a search warrant. He'd realised at long last what it was a penniless man could leave to his killer.

His name.

There was a life insurance policy found stashed away in Jagdev Rai's affairs; Warren knew that there would be. Rai had secretly taken out the policy in 2008 using Jasbir's full name and birth date. Jasbir was living in Canada at the time. Rai had only to pretend to be a man two years his junior, thirty-seven, whose thoughts, entering midlife, were turning to mortality, to providing for a loved one in the unlikely event something happened to him, since, despite excellent health and high spirits, you never knew, right?

The moment he'd come off the phone he became Jagdev Rai again. 'The beneficiary' Jagdev Rai.

Ever since, he'd been paying a £20 monthly premium for a policy presently valued at £318,913. Add to that the mortgage on a small house in Wednesbury he'd also taken out in the name of Jasbir Singh Bains. The accompanying life insurance was valued at a further £56,703.

In all, Jasbir's name, on Rai's papers, was worth over £375,000. Rai had been biding his time until the investigation blew over and he could put in his claim.

He was arrested in early April 2013 for the murder of Jasbir Singh Bains.

Warren and his team had learned that Jasbir had borrowed thousands of pounds from Rai, not long before flying to Canada. The flight had infuriated Rai; he'd made it known around town that he was more than unhappy about the debt. Now the police discovered that in June of the same year – 2006 – he'd used a deed poll to create a parallel identity for himself in the name of his future victim.

The accused refused to cooperate with the police. There'd been no hard feelings between him and the victim, he claimed. He would not say what he had done with the blade brought to the park that night, or with the dead man's phone he'd carried away. He would not say with which fateful words he'd texted Jasbir an invite to the park – perhaps something like, 'Meet u at the lake Jas, for old time's sake. Got some cans from the outdoor.'

Police used mobile network records to link Rai's text to

around the time of the killing. Their search of his house uncovered the phone packaging and SIM card holder of the device used to send the invite.

In January 2014 Rai's trial came to court and Warren was called to give evidence. The accused's continued denials did not surprise the detective. He'd seen and heard it all before. The lengths to which they would go to lie. Even when caught red-handed, even when in court, up before the judge in a borrowed suit and tie, swearing to tell the truth, the whole truth and nothing but the truth, they would lie. Stupid lies. Transparent, contradictory lies.

From the BBC News website, 21 February 2014:

A man has been jailed for life for slitting his friend's throat and dumping his body in a lake.

Jagdev Singh Rai, 44, of West Bromwich, was convicted of murdering Jasbir Singh Bains, 41, at Wolverhampton Crown Court.

Mr Bains was found floating in a lake in Dartmouth Park, West Bromwich, in November 2012.

Mr Rai, also known as Jamie, was sentenced to a minimum term of 27 years. He had denied the murder but was convicted on Thursday.

Warren retired from the West Midlands detective team in 2019. He wasn't getting any younger or fitter. Of the ninety-two murders he'd investigated over seven years, all but one ended in the killer's conviction. These days he works mostly from home, assessing officers for promotion. He passes on his experience to junior colleagues, future detective inspectors some of them, so that his knowledge will survive him. So that, in his own modest way, he'll leave a name that's worth remembering.

Naoise

Once I write this sentence I hardly know where it will take me, she thought as she sat at the crowded desk by the window and lifted her pen optimistically. All night she had slept on the sentence, which, she could see now in the frank light of day, was a definite improvement on its predecessor. And so she crossed out words long worked over and beneath them jotted down their betters, killing her darlings without qualms or regrets, for after all, as she often told herself, perhaps a little too often, they were only words. Head bent, busy pen in hand, she hoped to sit like this throughout the remainder of her time alone. But after an hour or so she felt her mind begin to wander. A daydream came between her and the pages, the last draft of her first novel, *Edith and Julian*, to which she was applying the final touches.

She was on the guest list of some swanky literature festival, perhaps up for a prize – this *was* a daydream, wasn't it? There she went, picture it, swanning her way to the entrance, dressed for the occasion (less so for the Tube rides) and already tasting the bubbly when she bumps smack-bang into the doorman. A smile. That is, a doorman's smile, the least smiley-looking smile around. 'Name, please.' That's what doormen say. Not hello or good evening. Name, please. A glance down at his list. 'Nee-sha Dolan,' she'd say, to which she'd get a perplexed, 'How do you spell that?' That's when she'd know she was well and truly out of Terenure. 'N-a-o-i-s-e.'

She shook her head then and found herself once more in the flat she shared with an asset manager who doubled as her best friend. They'd met at a university debating contest and got on so well that they had known straightaway they'd be in each other's life forever. Both now entering their late twenties, they had in common a certain estrangement, a sense of not quite belonging or fitting in. Both were new to London: his family were British Indian; hers, Irish. He fell in love with men; she, with women. Neither had what you might call a typical mind. 'Off in her own world,' people had always said of her, although her mother preferred to say 'imaginative'. She'd hid from schoolmates her swotty summers at the camps organised by the Dublin Centre for Talented Youth. It'd been a relief not having to hide any of this from her flatmate-slash-best friend – he'd earned eighteen A-stars at GCSE. A precocious history buff at thirteen, he'd volunteered to spend three weeks living in 1941 for a British TV documentary series. Smothering blankets. Tripe for supper, and stodgy apple pie. No computers or mobile phones. No communication with the outside world. It had been his idea of fun. Naoise, when told the story, thought it sounded like way too much trouble. She had also lived immersed in the forties, incommunicado for weeks – it was called reading a Jane Bowles novel.

Oh, but, this was no way to be working. Daydreams and distractions. Allowing her cloud-like thoughts to drift. She retrieved her pen and again faced the typescript pages and the emendations in her neat cursive. She felt she knew all these pages by heart. She knew where the words were long and made the reader pause, where laughs were caused by this scene or that pun. She knew the polished parts that had taken ages and ages to get just right. The wry observations on money, sex and class. The exchanges where she showed how her generation formed relationships, how they text-messaged, how they spoke. She saw the gap here on this page that no one else would know to see, the edited-out sentence (another darling gone) that had once filled it:

'He'd had a habit of cutting short whatever you were saying to go, Yeah, yeah, yeah, like he wanted to be agreeable but wished you could be slightly more economical with his time.'

Economical. It was her style as well.

She read over the pages, but she had not written in pages. She'd written paragraph by paragraph, sentence by sentence, word by word. Each one a swaying bridge to the next. All through the writing she'd avoided ideas of plot or character, but simply cultivated both as they'd grown out of the words that she selected – they were what happened when the words acted on one another, influenced one another, made sense together. Not once had she imagined a scene in order to write it, the shape of a table or the dimensions of a room or even colours – she didn't see red when she wrote 'red', rather she saw what writing 'red' would do to a sentence, and what the sentence would do to a scene, and what the scene would do to the story. In this associative, cumulative, almost magical way she had composed and now revised this debut novel of hers. It was how she knew to write.

To which genre, she wondered with some dry amusement, would critics assign *Edith and Julian*: Literary fiction? Young adult romcom? Highbrow chick lit? Chic lit? Aut lit? (Recently she'd had it confirmed from doctors that she was autistic.) She could be as ferocious with herself as with her words.

Dark humour – that ability to make light of yourself, of circumstances beyond your control – it had helped to save her more than once, growing up. Came with the family back in Ireland. Speaking of whom, what would they make of these pages once they were published next year? The book, they would call it. Never the novel. Your book. Her book. She could imagine her mother's friends sighting it in Eason's, saying to her mother afterwards, 'Hasn't your one done well for herself.'

Had she, though? She could not be so certain. She had the very bad habit of being hard on herself and here she went again. Two hundred or so pages. A slim novel. Versions of which, at least the earliest scenes, dated back four years. Four years, and this was all the writing she had to show for them. But this was unfair. It was her nature, and her wisdom, not to rush. And she was forgetting her piece of travel writing which had appeared in the Irish press. Not to mention her poem, 'Seasonal Fling', all seventeen lines of it, published by a culture website in her last year at uni. She had several short stories ready to go. Essays, too. And literary criticism.

Publishers were interested, that was the main thing. Seven of them in Britain had just bid for the rights to her novel.

The alarm on her phone alerted her to a coffee break. Gladly she took leave of the desk and made for the kitchen, suddenly recalling her legs. Bloody pins and needles. She hobbled over to the kettle, thinking it was a good thing the jar of instant hadn't moved. Where would she be without it? Not at this cupboard, that was for sure. From a low shelf, she fetched down her usual mug.

She was a creature of routine. A stickler for it, she might say. Every day began with her toothbrush, and afterwards there would be coffee but neither too soon – for then her enamel might stain – nor too late, lest she should grow too tired and headachy to do anything with her morning, including going out for coffee. That was why she always allowed thirty minutes – not twenty, or forty – between her tooth-brushing and her coffee drinking. Time enough to dress for the café and to rehearse ordering her customary soy flat white to go, and the trip to said café which would get her walking and the walking get her dopamine flowing through her brain. A long sip back at her desk, or two, or three, and she'd feel 'on', open her email briefly, then spread out her pages like a general with a map.

Quite often, though, the coffee wouldn't behave. It wouldn't want to stay put in the cup; it would dribble down the sides, spatter her skirt and leave moist brown rings on her manuscript.

Some days the novel had needed six cups or eight, other days, ten. All in all, gallons had gone into the book, she could have bathed in the stuff, like Cleopatra and her donkey milk – with the difference that coffee, at least, really was rejuvenating.

No coffee, no novel. It was as simple as that. Also: no reading, no novel – for reading had always seemed to her as vital as eating, and, as it happened, she trusted her own good taste in literary influences. Jane Bowles. She'd read, and reread, *Two Serious Ladies* during the months that she wrote an early draft, and taken from it various lessons in dialogue. And she'd paid just as great attention to her dog-eared Oscar Wilde, because could that Irishman write! Those plays, the evergreen wonder she'd found in them as a teen, the wonder of being initiated into other people's thoughts. She loved how Wilde's prose bared a character's innermost urges, condensing them into pithy phrases, excelling in telling without a story's saids and dids.

Nabokov. Another treasured model. The émigré's sharp eye and sure feel for language. Whenever she'd become despondent, mid-second or third or fourth draft or later, wondering if there was any point to what she was doing, or trying to do, with a sentence structure, or some allusion, she'd had only to revisit his *Lectures on Literature* to quell her unease.

'The inner texture of life is also a matter of inspiration and precision.'

She thought that she would like to travel again, once she had finished digesting these and other influences; she would like to drink cappuccinos in Florence and then take off wherever her public readings might lead her. Although these plans wouldn't be actualised any time soon. The publication date – April 2020 – seemed to her an eternity away. Scheduled for the week she'd turn twenty-eight – she hadn't long been twenty-seven. So, really, an eternity away! And nerve-shredding to imagine all that might come between her and the novel's release, between now and that faraway then. Her publisher might go bankrupt (though there was no reason in the world to think it would); global war might shatter cities; some third-floor piano, with Chopin open on it, might crash from a window onto her passing head. Odder things had happened, indeed were always happening somewhere.

Curious to think that copies of her novel would be read by perfect strangers up and down the counties of Ireland, across Britain, North America, and still other lands. Strangers who, turning its pages, might linger over this scene or sentence, that paragraph or chapter, and find them good. Better than good – striking, moving even.

She did not know if she believed in an ideal reader – and certainly did not write for such a person. She wrote for anyone who would read her with care.

Out of her difference, her singularity, she would speak to theirs.

Ask anyone in Dublin and they'll tell you that Terenure – in the Southside – is a grand place to live. Not far from Rathgar, where, in Jimmy O'Dea's lyrics, even those who can't afford it have a car.

People from Kimmage, though it abuts Terenure and is said to have gone up in the world in recent years, will agree that the latter is rather posh.

Quiet, Terenure's residents will say to describe the place. Boring more like it, grumble their teenagers. The sort of place where nothing much happens, young and old agree, though what each means by that is rather different.

Naoise's parents still live in the sought-after red-brick where she and her siblings were raised. Her father worked for the Electricity Supply Board. Her mother was a teacher and aromatherapist. Both parents valued the arts and there was always music in the house, the notes mingling with the bright smell of lavender. The music came especially from Naoise's mother's side, Longford people who sang in choirs and squeezed accordions. Her mother played the French horn and taught her shy daughter the euphonium.

All cows eat grass, her mother said. She was teaching Naoise to sight-read. A C E and G were the space notes: A(ll) C(ows) E(at) G(rass).

The euphonium took some learning to handle; it was a big brass instrument for a small girl. Doubtfully, Naoise brought the mouthpiece to her lips, puffed out her cheeks and blew for all she was worth. The euphonium seemed almost to hesitate. Then up writhed a lazy note, part complaint and part whisper, like the last breath of a deflating balloon.

She tried again and again and her face grew very red, a picture of furious concentration. Her stubbornness endeared her to any teacher. Did that girl ever persevere!

Then, one day, her hands warming to the brass, she poised her fingers on the valves and summoned her deepest breath. The note sounded deep and clear. A jolt of surprise went through her; she hadn't known her own eloquence.

With time and practice she spoke more fluently in the instrument's rich voice. Her intonation and phrasing improved. When she got to be good enough she played in a concert band and conversed with the trombones and promptly answered the clarinets.

None of this surprised her mother. Naoise had an inborn ear for rhythm, which had spurred her special gift for language. When still a toddler she would time her mother's index finger as it travelled the width and length of her bedtime story. If the finger lagged she squirmed, if it ran ahead she whimpered. She was placated only when finger and voice remained in tempo.

Soon after, she had learned to link the letters' shapes to their sounds; to read along, then, alone.

She would open her storybooks on her knees and read aloud to the empty bedroom, performing the stories' music in a solo recital. Lips pursed, she blew b's – like how her mother blew into a French horn – and the b's called up bats, and pulled down the black curtain of nightfall. Then she sucked in a lungful of air

86

to sound the o's and raise the moon. Tongue behind her front teeth, she played the l's and stars gleamed and sparkled and twinkled.

It seemed to her that the variations she could play with twenty-six letters were infinite.

Stories are infinite but not storybooks, which is why Naoise could soon be seen – though not heard – in the musty hush of the local library. On her first visit she stood two bookshelves tall, and feared she'd never reach the higher titles. For the longest time imaginable she was no taller than Religion. Astrophysics was way above her head. So was James Joyce.

It didn't take long to learn her way around, the library being rather compact. The solar system was on your right as you went in; the Siberian Shelf above a radiator. Joan of Arc in one aisle; Henry VIII in another. She often passed the Middle Ages, among whose volumes hid Death, wearing a white toga and looking famished.

Naoise checked out stories of people and places that did not exist. Castles that went bump in the night. Dribbling ghouls and zombies (the vibrations of the letter 'z' adding to their scare-appeal). A parallel universe of witchcraft and wizardry. She'd save them for after dark and the light of her bedside lamp, turn the pages faster and faster, racing sleep, until she could barely tell if she was reading or dreaming.

Freedom was the name for the dizzying power that lasted through her library expeditions. No pleasantries ever needing to be exchanged with the librarian on duty. Even the round clock at high noon on the wood-panelled wall had no claim on her. From the first second she entered the building she was in other times, other dimensions. She was other Naoises.

The Dolans' girl, people in Terenure said. Their eldest, they might have added. A freckly slip of a thing with a brown bob of hair, but that wasn't what people noticed. Fierce smart, they'd say. Smart as she was shy.

She never talked back in class. Hardly ever talked at all. She let her compositions do the talking for her, and her teachers when they read them out. Sure hated hearing herself in their voice as they pronounced her long words, 'vociferous' and the like, while doing their best to make each sound natural. What a blush she'd have on her then, willing herself to disappear. Please forget about me, leave me to my books, that blush said.

Still, it was a good primary for a pupil like her: Church of Ireland, open-minded staff and small, as in, four classes in the whole place. A dozen or so pupils to a class.

Too noisy, Naoise thought, when she heard the children playing together. It disappointed her that real life should be not one bit like *The Sims*. She'd made ten new friends that month on her PC, so why not any here? She wasn't her pixel self, was why, climbing the scale of outgoingness. Not that the flesh-and-blood girls in her class helped much, haring and squealing the instant they got out at break, the opposite of the sort of quiet playmates she'd have invented. And to think they called *her* rude when she preferred to sit still and read on a playdate. She didn't get it at all – there were more than enough books in her room for everyone.

She was terrible at reading faces or situations. Her blue eyes fled the eyes that surveyed her. Don't worry, the girls laughed, they were only messing with her. Laughing at something she'd just said. Blimey! Who says blimey? Only Naoise and Harry Potter, that's who.

Incessantly, she tried to parse the classroom's English, the other children's English, the children's playground chatter, their element.

Adults she crossed in the streets and shops were no easier to understand. Their talk was small and baffling. She'd heard the strange things they did with words. For instance, the neighbouring suburb's name of Ranelagh. Some said 'Ran-uh-la' (or Ran-la), others, 'Ren-uh-la' (or Ren-la). Why couldn't they agree? You'd think they lived in different places entirely, and not the exact same neighbourhood and sometimes street, whenever they gave out their address.

And it wasn't just the locals, Naoise had noted, it was the same with other English-speaking adults, tourists told to have a good day and who replied 'you too' in a British accent. Whereas people like her parents or her teachers invariably replied 'same to you'. Which was right or better, Naoise wondered, or was it a matter of circumstance? It made her fretful not knowing the rule, or even if there was a rule, because what if a tourist ever wished her a good day? She'd be lost for words.

Sometimes the mere sound of an adult's word could be as disconcerting. Her mother's words for certain foods, for example, made her appetite vanish. She had to be the only child in Ireland, so her mother complained, to shake her head at potato 'mash'. 'Porridge' she would not touch either – that is, not until years later, when she learned to think of it as 'overnight oats'.

It was different if her teacher said 'porridge' to the class, because this would be during a game, simply a word said aloud then and nothing you had to eat, or formulate a response to, or risk mispronouncing as a name. Simply a word, to savour and play with, and for this reason classmates and teacher were all of a sudden in *her* element for a change, and Naoise knew precisely what to do. In her mind, the word's letters shone, its bum note was pardoned. The game was dictionary-racing.

'Porridge,' said the teacher.

And his star pupil, who usually found this word's sound so distasteful, and heard him say it, beamed as she opened her dictionary straight to P. She was seconds from the entry. The trick was not to part the pages in the middle, but further along, about seven-tenths of the way in. There, got it!

Five seconds flat – go, Naoise!

There were other games. One autumn school day in the early noughties, towards the end of Naoise's time in primary, a new craze reached her playground. Everyone in sixth class, it seemed, was playing IRA. To an otherworldly eleven-year-old the name didn't shock. Naoise took in her classmates' instructions, listening intently. They were to divide themselves into opposing teams and each side to settle on a secret word – a word eight letters long if they played eight to a side – and each team member to become a letter in their word. So far so clear? Example: your team settles on 'porridge'. Then the first child becomes P, the second O, the third and fourth R, through to G and E. Each side's goal was to figure out the other team's word by chasing and cornering their opponents, and then to extract from each one the letter they were.

'Stop! I give up. Stop tickling. I'm G.'

'He's G!'

In some schools the game was banned after a boy in Kilkenny tumbled and broke his arm, but Naoise's classmates were far more sedate. No pinches, wrestling or tugging of hair. They executed good-humoured feints, wrong-footing their chasers, confessing their letters laughingly the instant they were caught.

Playing along, Naoise quite forgot her shyness. The once-squealing girls, the indifferent boys, were now vowels and consonants dancing in all directions, and she felt the same pull towards them as she did towards the sentences in her library books. She was A one day, V the next, and all around her the playground spun and when the craze fizzled out and the IRA game disappeared, Naoise knew she'd never play its like again.

When summer took Naoise out of primary, this time for good, the long days filled with the cracking of spines on old library hardbacks. She'd graduated to heftier tomes, the classics, 'improving' novels and the like; and having come to them on her own initiative, before any grown-up or curriculum could foist them onto her, she entered into them without any thought for the difference in age – hers and the books' – or indeed for their reputation as 'difficult'.

Her library carried plenty of Dickens – *David Copperfield*, *Bleak House*, *A Christmas Carol*, the works – as well as the Brontës and Eliot and Austen. Tall enough now, she pulled from the shelf one of the dustless classics which had left with half of Terenure's borrowers before her, a book that had ridden high on park swings and sunned in gardens and absorbed tea and tears in strangers' lounges, and when she opened its pages a smell of almonds greeted her, something like her mother's make-up, sweet and flaky.

She began to read:

'Emma Woodhouse, handsome, clever and rich, with a comfortable home and happy disposition seemed to unite some of the best blessings of existence and had lived nearly twenty-one years in the world with very little to distress or vex her.'

Of all the characters she met, she wanted most of all to be Emma Woodhouse.

She longed to become someone else, at least at regular intervals. There wasn't much fun, she thought, in being Naoise Dolan. The Naoise whose choice of words sometimes caused other children to titter, or the Naoise who was dropping things, left, right and centre, or the one who was always getting the wrong end of grown-ups' conversations. None of those Naoises interested her. She was glad at the idea that she might one day leave them all behind. Her body was beginning to alter. She craved adolescence, as much as she feared it, for all that it might make of her. Adolescence: it was a striking word, a confident word, how did a girl ever live up to it?

'How was school, Naoise?'

'Mam!'

'What?'

'Don't.'

Up her teenage daughter went. From her bedroom came the thud of a bag being dropped.

This was nothing new, for ever since Naoise had started at the High School (that was its name, the High School, Dublin), her mood had darkened. Along with her clothes. Black on black. And with them a full face of make-up that only accentuated her look of gloom. Hormones, people said. Typical teenage hormones. But no, it was more than that, her mother thought. Behind the disguise of an emo-obsessed adolescent she glimpsed confusion and brittleness.

The new school, her mother thought. The jump from 80 to 800 pupils. A jump in pressure too, given the thousands of euros in annual tuition fees. That might be part of it. And Naoise was sixteen now. Possibly some boy trouble? Not that she knew of. The vegan diet? She had nothing against it, Naoise having always been a fussy eater, but perhaps a pubescent girl – nearly a young woman – needed more, what was it, vitamin B-something or other.

Maybe, just maybe, it was related to all the time her daughter was spending on her phone and laptop. Simply accessing the news in 2008 was enough to depress the stoutest heart. Crisis. Crash. Slump. A global recession we must start preparing for. That was the prediction of the *Irish Independent*. 'Hundreds of Staff Face Axe', cried every second or third headline.

Her mother didn't know. She didn't know what to think. None of the above explained the sunglasses in November, or the hugs from relatives her daughter always found too tight. None of it explained how she was with other teenagers, in the agonies of indecision, wanting every conversation – online and off – to end and never to end, and worrying, once it did, what she'd done to cause it to do so. No wonder, however rote or trite, these conversations robbed her of all her energy. Some mornings even the shower was too far. She rarely finished what she started – a meal, a sentence – with the fortunate exception of homework.

Hey, Thursday, Naoise thought in her room, could you try not being quite so awful next week?

She lay her head on the pillow and closed her eyes and listened through earphones to the songs emo girls listen to. Tegan and Sara. Radiohead. The raw, melancholic songs absorbed her as novels did. She mouthed along to the lyrics as outside the Dublin rain drummed on the roofs of Terenure, on the managers and consultants returning home from their offices.

Naoise was soon reflecting on how hard-up she was, how dull and plain, hemmed in by her little life, compared with her latest obsession, Blair Waldorf. Oh, Blair! High maintenance and worth her weight in gold. A different role model to Emma Woodhouse, but no less appealing. Naoise never missed an episode of *Gossip Girl* – the gorgeous women waltzing fragrantly out of a cocktail bar, into the Manhattan sun, every inch of them polished to a sheen, draped in designer garments, the world their oyster. In every shot, they made a fashion show of their wardrobes. Blair's clothes in particular were just wow: the pumps were Louboutin, her blouses Moschino, her dresses Marc Jacobs. The character luxuriated in her showy confidence.

Nothing gave Naoise more pleasure than admiring that confidence; she relished the cast's zippy one-liners and their debonair talk: no one ever simply had nothing to wear, they had 'fashion emergencies'. Orange juice in a mimosa they called 'OJ'. To 'have moves' was to dance well.

She found herself entertaining vague schemes to make money. Enough not to have to think about money. Buy dollars cheap and sell later at higher prices – that sort of thing. Majoring in economics might be a wise investment. She began to think of all the people she might invite, or disinvite, to her imaginary champagne brunch.

The other, rawer, show she couldn't miss in those days was *Skins* – it dazzled her how the teenage characters let their every thought hang out. The storylines had it all: sex, drugs, moody music, expletives and dramatic flashbacks.

Certain evenings, after an episode, she opened Word on her laptop and transposed the characters from Bristol to Ireland, giving them new names and similar problems, sketching scenes and trimming them, feeling a furtive joy such as she was to know half a dozen years later when, far away from here, she began drafting *Edith and Julian*.

Wasn't she young, well-meaning voices said, didn't she have her whole life in front of her. But that was not a thought to put Naoise's mind to rest.

'Smile, love. It might never happen.' But soon 'it' did. Her difficulties felt insurmountable. Writing. Reading. Homework. Daily functioning. She wasn't in the right headspace for anything. There were always too many things that needed doing: washing, swallowing, choosing, answering, filling in. Not that she didn't know where to start. She knew where to start. That wasn't the problem. The problem was having to mentally review every single action, in sequence and exhausting detail, on the days when habit stood her up.

Nine a.m., ten a.m., sometimes all through a morning, she stayed in bed, immobile – it felt like such a trek even to her toothbrush. Her head ached, then throbbed. Possibly she was thirsty. She remembered listening to a doctor explain to her that moods go up and down. Whenever she was feeling low, the woman had said, she made some me-time for herself. She curled up to easy listening or had a good long soak in the bath.

Naoise told another doctor about her anxiety, her sleeplessness. Turning in at midnight only for her body clock to choose 3 a.m., of all hours, to rouse her. Counting down then from 500, getting all the way down to zero. Wide awake still, she'd lie on her side, her eyes squeezed tight, for as many minutes as her prodding thoughts would allow, and then turn over and repeat, over and bloody over again, until the thoughts at last released her, or else exhaustion overran them.

This wasn't a phase, she learned. But, rest assured, there were treatments available. And small adjustments which, combined, could add up to a big difference. Reducing her screen time for one.

She heard this doctor say 'autism spectrum' and 'a possibility'.

'What are you reading?' Reluctantly, Naoise looks up and responds, 'Nothing.' She has played out this scene in her mind a hundred times before. The man – for it is always a man – fidgets in his bus seat, his face plump and perspiring. Or he is skinnier, nearer her age and chatting to her on some stupid dare probably. Or he's someone who could be her grandfather, arthritic legs apart, a cane between his knees.

She is reading *Great Expectations* by Charles Dickens, but that is nobody's business but her own, and perhaps the college library's. As it is, she must drop the book to her lap, then into her bag, and wait for any impudent-looking man to alight at the next stop, or the stop after that, before resuming. While she waits, she glares down at the flats of her empty palms as though reading them.

Naoise

The blue and yellow double-decker is inching towards Trinity College Dublin; its other passengers stare blankly at their phones or at their reflections in the dirty panes. The space beside her is taken by her bag. 'Not much of a talker are you?' says the man, whichever one he is. She hates riding the bus. She hates the scrums at rush hour and the teenage boys who snigger or shout 'queer' when they pass The George. She hates the men who threaten to break in on her concentration. On her free time.

Plenty of Trinity students rode this bus, but Naoise, a senior fresher, soon preferred to cycle the thirty-minute route with its honking motorists to negotiate, the passing cars that sent up spray. She toughed out the awful rain, cold and clinging. It was only rain after all. She'd known worse, though some days it really lashed down. Only rain, it couldn't help being wet. And besides, she wasn't made of sugar.

For years before she went, Naoise was going to university. With a head like hers there had never been any question of her not going. The only question had been whether she would go to Trinity, as everyone recommended she do, given her grades in English, her love of thick books, or to an art college, since she also had her father's eye (he was an amateur photographer) and loved to draw. By way of compromise she became a 'Trinner' and contributed drawings, as well as articles, to the student newspaper.

In her junior freshman year she read French and Russian. She found quite a few of the sentences unreadable. They defeated her. Ivan Velikopolsky, the son of a something, and a student of the something academy, returning home from something, kept walking on the path by the something meadows. There was Russian's strange alphabet (though she'd dabbled in both Japanese and Arabic for a time online), but grammar was the bigger obstacle. The French subjunctive, the Russian dative, not that either would have been insuperable, for she enjoyed the time spent in another language – she had some Irish – and her reserves of patience were large. Simply, she couldn't resist it any longer.

English. Which, to her mind, had always been a charmingly, frustratingly foreign language as well. She'd spent twenty years reading it, so why not four more? It proved to be a sound decision, not least because of her long acquaintance with many of the assigned works, so that her essays earned high marks while not requiring too much thought, and also because it left her time to prep for a new-found passion she'd discovered: college debating.

This House would occupy Wall Street.

This House believes that it is always immoral to kill another human being.

This House regrets Lara Croft.

College debating was a world largely of young men, sons of Dublin 4, loud with bow ties and rowdy 'points of information'. But it was also a world in which clarity and precision of speech were prized. Naoise was a fast learner; the verbal jousts enlivened her imagination. She drew facts and ideas from the relevant parts of her brain at a split-second's notice, and for her allotted seven minutes in a debate she could hold the room. Her hands grew animated as she spoke, pulling at the air around her face, bunching and uncurling fingers. Listening, her opponents and audience looked up past the fingers at her experiment in red hair, at her spiky spectacles, her colourful neck wraps, which were all a part of her evolving style.

Dressing snappily, speaking her mind, the brassy persona she adopted in these debates owed more than a little to Blair Waldorf. Owed something also to John, her debating partner, floppy-haired and bright-eyed, who spoke with the verve of a lawyer's son, the force of an ambassador's grandson.

John Prasifka. What kind of a name was that, people who heard it wondered. Russian? No, it wasn't Russian. It was Moravian. Czech we would say today. Prašivka, perhaps John had been told or learned online, is a word still heard in Czechia. It can refer to a dusty room, much like the kind in which he and Naoise conducted their debates. Primarily, though, it describes a certain type of mushroom, puffballs filled with brown or grey spores, or others that pickers don't know what to make of, and so leave alone.

'Don't get him started on God and free will,' John's mates warned.

Like Naoise, he could lose himself in thought. Theology and numbers and equations – the more abstract, the better.

Naoise knew John's girlfriend, Sally, an ace debater herself, who was two years above her in English. They flew far and wide, Naoise and John and Sally, representing the College's colours in international debating contests. Galway, London, Cambridge, Edinburgh (where Naoise's future best friend and flatmate was studying), Venice, Helsinki, Belgrade, Malaysia – she racked up more miles than Phileas Fogg. Everywhere she was met by new questions to take apart, the ping-pong of arguing points, a hall's applause singling out her sharpest responses. Her best results would go up on social media, prompting classmates to text that they were just after seeing them. Fantastic. Brill. Well done.

You might imagine that she was living the high life, but she wasn't really. All those ultra-low-cost flights at ungodly hours. Hotel windows which afforded only views of drainpipes. But at least, for a few days at a time, she was leaving Dublin behind her. Overseas were the great rolling hills and cityscapes that offered relief to her eye. Food and drink tasted better in Finnish, Serbian, Malay.

More and more these days she was living in the future, which she placed abroad. What about here, she thought, or here, or here, getting warmer as she travelled further east. She put in this future glamorous dresses and heels high enough to be murder on cobblestones – but so worth it – and shiny buildings that rose and rose until they scraped the sky, their many stories lifting her out of herself.

September 2016. Word quickly got around that Sally had a novel coming out. No really. It had been announced in the press and everything. It had gone to Faber and Faber.

Naoise was in Singapore when the news reached her. How mad to picture the name of John's girlfriend on a book cover: Sally Rooney.

Naoise had quit Ireland with her bags and degree a few weeks earlier, having grown bone-tired of Terenure, wanting nothing more than for the home town to make itself scarce, vacate the space it occupied in her life and leave it to some far-flung place more promising. English was what had brought her out here, teaching it paid good Singapore dollars. Between the classes she could go sightseeing, shouldering a backpack with zip pockets for keys and snacks and the funny money, a round flask pocket, pockets to keep her passport and other papers dry and legible, pockets for the pockets.

That was the plan anyway. But haze – like smog in a Dickens novel – had set in and the island lay under a mist of acrid smoke. And then she learned that teaching English – specifically, early literacy – paid even better Hong Kong dollars.

So it was that Hong Kong became the backdrop of the story she began to write there to fill her weekends and hours off: the pawnbrokers' neon lights and the hilariously tall buildings and the MTR underground she rode with her Octopus card while a lady's voice intoned 'mind the gap' in Mandarin, Cantonese and English. She wrote in cafés, careful not to upset her coffee. She started small – a few lines of dialogue, a sketch of a street corner – and let the pages multiply. Everything around her seemed to feed her writing. One time, at a rooftop bar, a row of hooks at a standing table snagged her attention. Where other women hung their handbags she hung a scene in her story.

On some days the sentences flowed and she could write nothing wrong; on others the words seemed to drown in their own ink and the delete key became her friend.

With these eye-hooking details and astute deletions, page by page Naoise built her paper Hong Kong. For months she lived happily there, in a city under her own construction, moving streets and shops around her chapters, and changing a bookstore's green door on Park Road to red when red suited the scene better.

Ava was the name Naoise gave her story's narrator – something a barista might write on a customer's cardboard cup when that customer was called Éabha – Irish for Eve. If Ava wasn't Naoise, the resemblance was nonetheless strong: Ava was only slightly younger than her twenty-four-year-old creator, and taught slightly older Hong Kong children English. Naoise put her circuitous thoughts into Ava's head, and her sometimes spellcheck-defying words – like defalcatory and procacious – into Ava's mouth. But in other ways character and creator differed. Ava's love interests – the story's title characters, Edith and Julian – were hers alone.

In the story, Ava shares her life and bed with Julian, a wealthy English banker, but her heart belongs to a new friend, Edith Zhang Mei Ling, whose name promises the change (the 'edit') Ava needs. Alphabetically and emotionally, Ava is closer to Edith than to Julian. All the pages of Naoise's writing, then, turned on the question: would Ava accept her feelings and choose her soulmate?

Towards the end of her year in Asia, a large envelope came for Naoise, red and regal with English stamps and postmarked Oxford. Shaky hands. Then a different shaky: she'd been accepted into the Victorian Literature MA programme. A pinch of her arm reassuringly hurt. So she packed her story and clothes and flew to read the Greats in the shadow of spires, and in other cafés continued to write and cut and revise.

Sally was sent an excerpt. When not being literature's next big thing she was editing the *Stinging Fly*, a literary journal, and gave an enthusiastic thumbs up to publish. Naoise read what became her novel's second chapter in the summer 2018 edition, under the title 'Autumn in Hong Kong'.

It wasn't long before a literary agent approached her. The novel needed only a few more tweaks before it could be published whole. Naoise went down to London to share a flat while she made ever finer revisions.

✳

I wanted something to read on the train. My Eurostar wasn't leaving St Pancras for another couple of hours, so I went into the station's bookshop, down the end to Fiction and found the Dolan on the top shelf, sandwiched between Doerr and Donoghue.

Edith and Julian was still the title in Swedish (*Edith och Julian*), but here, as in most of the dozen or more countries where the novel has appeared, the plush front cover said *Exciting Times*.

This bright, blocky cover had become a familiar sight to me over the course of the Covid pandemic; an Internet word-of-eye success during the time when physical bookstores had been forced to close. I saw it in online reviews (generally, very positive) which sent me to e-commerce sites informing me that readers who liked *Exciting Times* also liked *The Hunger Games*, *The Bell Jar* and *Normal People*.

I saw it in coverage of all the awards the debut novelist had been nominated for: the Women's Prize and the Dylan Thomas Prize, the Sunday Times Young Writer of the Year, among others.

I saw it in pictures that ran with the novelist's interviews with the press, in which she spoke openly about the neurodiversity she and I share.

After seeing these, I had managed to get a message to her on social media. An author myself, I had the idea of writing about her formative years leading up to her novel.

She was buried under interview requests from everywhere, and up against a tight deadline for a second novel, but Naoise was kind enough to email me several anecdotes from her childhood. I read these and her years of social media posts, alongside the essays and short stories and articles she'd published in various media. On the Eurostar back to Paris one evening, I began to read her book. The instagrammable sentences and very short chapters and vivid wordplay kept the pages turning swiftly.

Naoise Dolan's second novel came out in May 2023. In her black-and-white author photo she looks sultry, glamorous, marvellously composed.

Billy

One moment, the boy was standing twice, thrice, four times his mother's height; the next, the top of his head hardly came up to her chin. He was playing on the trampoline.

His mother, Eve, liked nothing better than to stand back and watch. Particularly now, in the still good light of a long summer evening. She craned her neck to see her son's figure high in the barn (that wasn't a barn but his playhouse), energised by the trampoline, sailing his limbs through the currents of air, which were warm-smelling and mote-speckled. Up he would jump, the soles of his shoes leaving the taut mat and showing their grooves, his arms outstretching, the rising T-shirt disclosing the small of his back, the cheeky belly button. Up and down went Eve's head, up and down, nodding along. Every time she thought he had crested he would soar another inch or more and reach new heights. His mop of blond hair stood on its ends at his zenith. An infectious grin widened his face.

That's my boy! That's my Billy!

To unsuspecting onlookers he would have seemed much like any other North American boy, well-fed and rosy-cheeked, deeply absorbed in his happiness, knees scabby below the shorts which ballooned with every leap. But had they looked again, and closer, they might have seen the signs, small but telltale.

A slight rigidity in the limbs. The fixed gaze. Six knots laced tight over the tongue of each shoe.

It was quite the relief for Eve to see him come back down to earth, in a final ceremonious thud, and resume the height of an eight-year-old.

One day in the mid-1980s, Eve lifted the hefty receiver to her ear and dialled a familiar number. When the ringing ceased and her mother picked up, Eve knew that she would tell her everything. Her mother had the quiet authority of the city mayor she would later become; her Tennessee vowels – unaltered by her family's years in Cleveland Heights, Ohio – could get all sorts of anecdotes, admissions, reminiscences out of her eldest daughter. It never ceased to amaze Eve that when she was little, her mother sat in her pew every Sunday and did not say a thing. Not even a prayer aloud to praise the Lord's word. Then the sixties happened. Eve's parents exchanged their church for one in a YWCA basement, where babies bawled and women preached. The first Sunday her mother spoke in public she sounded as though she had gained an octave. A voice hitting its stride, the same clear and purposeful one Eve was addressing now over the phone.

She told her mother what the weather was doing in Massachusetts. Nothing special. They were expecting heavy rain later that week. She couldn't wait for the sun.

'Evie, is anything the matter?'

'I'm OK, Mom. I'm just feeling kinda bored, I guess.' Her

days were too long, her routines too familiar, the foreseeable future threatening to resemble too much the recent past.

'You know you can tell me anything.'

'I'm ... bored,' Eve said again. Even to her own ears, the admission was rather surprising. Her marriage of several years, to her college sweetheart, was happy. Their situation was more than good: Matt had made partner at an asset management firm in Boston; she was teaching theology at Thayer Academy. She had interesting thoughts enough, and free time to read and think and wonder. She wondered about agape, about unconditional love. She wondered what Jesus had meant when he said, 'Be perfect, therefore, as your heavenly father is perfect.'

Was it all the hours spent at a desk? Marking her students' papers was getting old. She should go out more, her mother suggested. Volunteer. Start getting her hands dirty. Her mother led by example, making and delivering sandwiches for the homeless.

But Eve, though she admired the example, and was touched and moved by it, was not her mother. She felt dedicated to her life of the mind, even as she half feared it was the only life she might ever know.

When she hung up the phone, she had no idea the explanation for her restlessness was already inside her. A first pregnancy – 1986. That was Ben. And three years later she became pregnant with Billy, who did not give her half as much trouble his brother had – none of the morning sickness or the swollen feet. She even had a good appetite; carrying Billy made her hungry. She craved tender cuts of meat. Grilled, broiled or fried. Medium-well.

Billy was born on 23 November, Thanksgiving Day, during a snowstorm. The snow was quite something that day, even by New England's standards.

It was Christmas in Cleveland Heights, PBS was showing *The Snowman* and Billy sat hypnotised. Bar the theme song's lyrics, no one said a word in the animated film or its audience, whose members included Billy's grandparents, aunties and cousins. He had just turned six the month before; he was all eyes and ears before the pictures and music on the screen. The family knew what to get him for his next birthday. They didn't wait until then.

He wore that VHS down to the spool, never tired of watching it. Some years it seemed Christmas came every month, every week, to his home TV. You couldn't change channels whenever *The Snowman* was playing, even if the remote on the sofa's arm was flirting with you non-stop. You could only sit back and watch and try and see and hear what Billy saw and heard.

The pensive piano as a red-haired boy wakes to snow. Joyful flutes and pyjama jumps. Rush of dressing and racing outdoors. Drumbeats of deep footsteps, a snowball thrown awry, cross finger wagging at the window, retreating black tracks through the white lawn.

The boy makes a man out of the snow. Floppy green hat and scarf, an orange subtracted from the fruit bowl for a nose, black coal for eyes and buttons. The sweep of a finger to draw a smile. The mother's long shadow beckoning the boy in for bed.

Midnight. Whispery bells as he tiptoes downstairs to find the snowman come to life. A warm welcome indoors to admire the Christmas tree (how round the snowy face in the bauble) and try on different noses at the fruit bowl: pug (a cherry), big (a banana), laughable (a pineapple). The snowman basking in the fridge's yellow rays. His trombone sneeze after smelling the mother's perfume.

Billy

Throbbing violins as the two uncover the father's motorbike in the yard; an acceleration of horns as they zoom behind the golden cone of beam through woodland. The yellow-red of fox, brown of horse. Return to the garage. Then boy and snowman run into the air, to piano thunder and high-pitched song. Gliding fields of white, houses like those of dolls, roving cliffs and hills and peaks of ice, fuzz of pine forest, fireworks of Northern Lights. After the soft landing, the red round Santa, festive flutes and rattles as boy and snowman dance. Muted music for the flight home. The snowman in his garden, the boy in his bed. Then, in the bright sun of morning, the snowman is gone.

When he wasn't watching its celluloid twin, Billy was out in the real snow. The snow could just as agreeably be sleet or plain cold rain as far as he was concerned. He'd slow his pace in any downpour, not speed up as others do to find shelter. He'd slow to a crawl and instead of bowing his head he'd face the sky, feeling the drops pummel his temples, hearing them tambourine in his ears.

It was a similar story with the wind, which, for many Americans, exists as star-spangled banners flapping on poles. Or as tornados on TV. But for Billy the wind was alive. He would take it in his arms, dance with it, swaying and laughing. He never shunned it, never turned his back, when it blew hard.

During most of the first two years, Billy's infancy resembled Ben's.

As a baby he returned his mother's smile – he'd submit to her cooing and break out that grin of his, the one that made Eve think of her father when he played hearts at the kitchen table.

He had the Edwards men's energy about him too: exuberant, a robust character, Eve liked to say, rambunctious.

Eve said to Matt, 'He's got your hair and eyes.'

Mommy and Daddy. Juice. Sword. These were some of the only fifty or so words that Billy ever learned to say. Sword, because, at eighteen months, he played with a long plastic sword. Eve would remember that morning he'd held his toy aloft and said its name. Said it clearly. Not the easiest word for a boy his age to say, she had thought.

Many days during Billy's second spring Eve took him in the stroller along the woodland trails near their home.

'Look, Billy, moss!'

'Look,' said Billy.

And after he had sunk his baby fingers into it, Eve said, 'Soft, huh? Just like your cushion.'

That smell, she might say, was skunk cabbages flowering in the damp ground. And that whistling sound in the maple was a robin singing. The bird sang, *cheerily, cheer up, cheer up, cheerily, cheer up.*

He listened attentively. He smiled and giggled and responded to everything around him.

But within weeks, at home or outside, Billy altered. The change announced itself by a gradual silencing. Billy was losing words.

Perhaps it was all in her head. She'd misheard. But no, it wasn't, she hadn't. Well then, he was losing them momentarily, to a bad mood or a head cold. So he'd swallowed 'cookie' and dropped his 'cup' and mislaid his 'car'. Any day now he would utter them again, and others besides.

Only, once lost, the words never returned. 'Milk' and 'hi' and 'thank you' and 'all gone'.

Billy

He was assessed twice.

The doctor at Massachusetts General Hospital, all starch and stethoscope, couldn't find anything wrong. Billy's ears were fine, his coordination was fine. He knew as well as any two-year-old how to get a cookie out of his mother.

'He's not what you think,' the doctor said, when Eve raised the possibility of autism. He sounded very sure of himself.

Eve didn't know what to think.

A slow developer, people said, boys sometimes are. Give him a bit more time to straighten out. More time didn't help. What bothered Eve as much as the missing words, or more, was that Billy wasn't his grinning, charming self. He didn't react when she cooed; and, sometimes, as she went to touch him he made an angry sound, shrilling. Then she sat beside him and felt the rawness of his senses, the absence of language's second skin as he retreated from her, as if he had been stung.

Dr Margaret Bauman was different from her colleague. The first doctor had spoken too quickly, she said. Billy's symptoms were consistent with autism. Eve tried her best to listen as Dr Bauman explained. A developmental disorder of brain function, not a disease. Certain features become apparent over time, notably delayed use or absence of language. Intelligence on nonverbal tests may be in the normal or above-normal range. A condition of constant ups and downs, setbacks are common. Until that instant, Eve believed she had prepared herself to hear what the doctor was telling her.

Afterwards, while Billy slept in the car, she drove the long way back to the house. She could cry with abandon here, her crying swallowed up by the noises of the road. She could feel a strange gratitude for the orange cones, the construction work, that delayed her.

She was afraid. There had been some talk of an institution. A chill passed through her as she pictured her son imprisoned within himself, left to his own panic and confusion in the dark corner of a room.

Autism. Neurodevelopmental. A child quiet and withdrawn described as being 'on the spectrum'. Words later widely heard and spoken, but which sounded obscure in 1992, muffled within the heavy covers of manuals bearing forbidding titles, in closed-door conferences for specialists only, in reams of journal paper in German or jargon equally impenetrable.

She did not know the first thing about autism (or only the first, not the second or third). She remembered a movie she had seen, not the recent *Rainman* starring Dustin Hoffman, but an old French film in black and white. *L'Enfant sauvage* by François Truffaut. When had that been? During her college days at Chapel Hill. She would sometimes go to the little arts cinema there which showed pictures from Europe. Fellini. Bergman. The French new wave.

It was the boy in the film, the 'wild child', that Eve remembered, an infant abandoned to the woods of revolutionary France and whom a doctor, several years later, takes in. Her eyes would not leave the boy as the doctor tried teaching him to dress, sit in a chair, hold a spoon. No subtitles came up when the boy's sensitive face filled the screen, because he never would learn to speak. Too late. Too late for language.

The child's awful silence was the true star of these scenes, it seemed to Eve, a character in its own right, a baddie upstaging the youngster and drowning out all his lines. 'All ears on me,' the Silence cried. 'Fear me and shudder for the boy.'

Reading the newspapers – articles Eve would have previously skipped or skimmed – was enough to endorse a mother's worst fears. Two autistic pupils in Japan had died of heat prostration after their principal locked them in a windowless storage shed for two days. 'Strange and disquieting' was how a report in the *Washington Post* described a group of autistic children.

And then a fierce determination succeeded her initial shock, a craving for facts, knowledge, understanding. Hardly an hour now passed, half an hour, a quarter, without her thinking about Billy, and every spare minute not spent on calls from her siblings, or parents – how are you all holding up, Evie? – went into driving to and from, and combing through, bookstores, then returning home with the wares to read. None of the refrigerator mothers rubbish that you could still find then on certain shelves. Instead, Temple Grandin and Oliver Sacks. (How well, how thoughtfully, he could write about his subjects, and then, in the pages that interested Eve, how cruelly. One passage compared two autistic men, twins, to pantomime puppets.)

But there is hope, she thought, when she read about Clara Park and her daughter Elly. This was an old book, an expanded, updated reprint of Clara's memoir of Elly's early years, *The Siege*, which had first been published in the sixties. Eve had been drawn to the cover, the black-and-white photo showing a small child with fair hair and eloquent eyes, the mother looking through thick glasses at her offspring, protective and professorial. Elly's parents were both academics in Williamstown. Eve recognised the name – Williamstown is on the western side of Massachusetts (her own family lives on the eastern side). Like Billy, Elly had grown more or less silent by the age of two, devoting herself to her senses to the exclusion of people, playing by herself in ways that quickly became repetitive. But the Parks had not despaired. They had taken Elly to England, London, to 21 Maresfield Gardens and the Hampstead Clinic where they had received no end of reviving encouragement. Their efforts during their year in England, and then back in the US, to play and play and play with their daughter, in competition with her inwardness, to school and to stimulate her with pictures and gestures, signs and words, had been enormous. They would be compensated. Elly would grow more responsive, to the point of finally recovering her speech (though never speaking with much fluency). By the end of the book, Elly was a young woman who painted houses (that is, she painted beautiful, multicoloured pictures of houses she saw), and was holding down a job as a part-time mail clerk. She still lived with her parents, requiring constant care and supervision, and always would.

The last word in the book, in Elly's story, was 'love'.

Eve read its pages several times, though she knew it would not be sensible to get her hopes up too much. Billy wasn't Elly. His name wasn't in a book.

Outside the family circle she shared next to nothing about Billy, her thoughts and cares turned towards her son and home, her hope hugged tight.

Word would get out, though. It was only a matter of time. Soon neighbours would stop her in the street, or turn away, embarrassed, as she passed. The nosiest might sneak looks of commiseration at her son. How could she show her face in church? They would all crowd around, get in her way and on her nerves, the well-intentioned pity in their voices, saying, 'So sorry for you and Matt,' 'anything we can possibly do,' 'he's still your son,' and the furrows across their brows, aiming for solemn. She didn't want to be asked again and again how Billy was doing, or what the doctors had said or which treatments might be undertaken.

She put on her best face and let no one see a thing. She

continued favouring clothes that flattered, making the most of her thick curls, wearing earrings that caught and dispersed the light as they dangled. Creams and powder masked the angry red blotches that invaded her cheeks and nose and forehead – the months of stress and anguish catching up with her.

Therapists. Special educators. After Dr Bauman, she consulted widely. She canvassed their views, opinions, advice. She asked them to help her help Billy learn to tie his shoes, recognise words and, why not, use a computer one day – it being the nineties and everything. The specialists listened. They leaned back in their chairs then forward and said she should lower her expectations. They said this as if she had suggested something outlandish. Tie his shoes? Velcro would do the job.

Eve persevered. She asked what she might do to support her son more generally. What did she mean? She meant help him learn to communicate so as to be a full member of the family and society. And grow into a thoughtful, attentive young man. The specialists shook their heads. Hadn't her doctor explained what Billy's condition entailed? He would probably never learn to speak. Not speak, she said. She hadn't said learn to speak. Communicate. Surely Billy could be taught in some other way to communicate his needs, wishes, thoughts.

What thoughts? asked the specialists.

Their goal was to teach him to comply, she was told.

Anger and surprise took turns inside her. But why was she surprised? It wasn't like she had been born yesterday; she had met this attitude before, most often in men. 'You've got me all wrong,' she wanted to say. 'Me and my son.' She feared they were making a naive fool of her, one of those deluded women who blindly swears her child can do anything; why couldn't they see that she was for real? Imperfect, like any mother, she would allow, but always serious. And stubborn. Excuse her if she didn't bow down at once and truckle to their cold-eyed pessimism.

Family lore said Eve had always been something of a rebel. Her aunts liked to repeat the story of the time long ago when she and her sisters had stayed at Grandma Edwards'. The grandma could be stern, and she and Eve, who must have been nine or ten, hadn't seen eye to eye. Eve told her sisters, who had just received a scolding, to pick up their things and follow her. Chin held high, she escorted the sisters several blocks to the bus stop, put them and herself on the next bus, and rode home.

So before the specialists were even done saying all that her son would likely never learn to do or be, Eve had determined to prove them wrong. Big time.

I listen to Eve Megargel in Framingham as she gives her key-note and am glad I found her name. I have a fairly good view of her from where I'm sitting. She can't see me, though, not at all, even were she to scan every audience member at the back; I'm sitting further away still from the stage, five years away in the future, not to mention the little thing of the Atlantic Ocean between us.

Time and space concertinaed. The Internet can be wonderful like that. I close the video and send Eve an email asking whether she'd have some time to answer my questions. I tell her I'd like to write about them: her and her now adult son Billy. I don't tell her about my writer's block. A book has been waiting in my head for me to wrap up years of research, assume my ambitions, and commit it to paper. It is a collection of stories, real-life narratives that will explore the neurodiverse experience from many angles, with scenes and themes whose success will depend on my finding, for each story, the right form and face and voice.

After an exchange of messages, Eve and I find dates in our diaries to video-call regularly. Which we do over several months.

I watch home movie footage of Billy at three, six–seven, at ten, as a teen and young adult.

I learn all about electronic augmentative and alternative communication systems.

I feel words quicken and travel inside me, to the tips of my grateful, typing fingers.

The rest is this story.

I haven't any idea whether Eve knows very much about me, whether she has read any of my books, whether she sees any of Billy's autism in mine. I'm drawn to his experiences partly because they are so different.

I live by words, make my living from them, but sentences and syntax – as we define these traditionally – do not belong in Billy's language. His way of thinking and feeling and perceiving bypasses words. This inarticulacy has nothing to do with any lack of intelligence or curiosity or the desire to reach out to others. It has to do with an inner world that is pictorial, musical, and the many meanings he is able to find in shape, colour, motion, tone and rhythm.

Chess players, those with a facility for the game, access their own inner world – the chequered board and its pieces – somewhat like this. Not like a beginner, who loses himself in internal monologues as he contemplates the next moves; his patzer's prolixity – bishop up a row, take, take, if knight goes there, castle – is more muddling than enlightening.

In bright tensions, lines of pure energy, structures – that is how the grandmaster thinks.

'They just don't get it,' said Eve, one Sunday afternoon when her parents were over for lunch. By 'they' she meant some of the staff at Billy's school. 'I take Billy's device in to show the teacher and she's like, "What's the point? Look at all those buttons. He won't know how to use this." Trust me, he does. Just give him some encouragement. Then she goes, "Perhaps you think he does but anyways we don't go in much for these gadgets in class." Well, then, I say, I guess there's no time like the present to change that. "Mrs Megargel, we hear you." I'm not sure you do hear me. "We absolutely do." So I bite my tongue and I say to her, please do as I ask. Let Billy have his device with him in lessons. It's on her desk. She picks it up like it's mega heavy and it isn't heavy at all. "Okay, we'll give it a try," she says. "No promises, but we'll give it a try." Hallelujah!'

Come what may, the world could be sure of one thing: she would never give up on her son. She did not know the meaning of 'give up on her son'. He was their ward, hers and Matt's, would always be; anyone who imagined her beat and dejected couldn't be more mistaken. He would not be shoved to the margins, his potential left to moulder until it vanished – she would not allow it.

For several years now Eve had been following the advice in Clara Park's book almost to the letter. She had found a local school with the resources to take children like Billy, the classes small, the teachers and assistants well trained (though even there, she sometimes ran into resistance). The school had started Billy on pictures, a technique involving picture cards; the child learned to give a card to the adult to ask for or say the item shown. The images were bright, rudimentary, the word for each printed underneath. A stick man with a yellow book ('read'), a beige biscuit with a glass of milk ('snack'), a big red cross with downcast face ('no'). Some of the pictures illustrated words taken from American Sign Language. Flattened hands touching fingertips ('more'), a circular hand sweep around the chest ('please'). Billy did not use any sign language yet though. For a long time he could not point a finger or imitate.

At the age of five he had his first speech-generating device, a Macaw, positively prehistoric in comparison to later models. It was serviceable but clunky, and not very much to look at.

'He'll get the hang of it,' Eve had told Matt and Ben and herself, though she knew that was anything but certain. She had furnished the Macaw with pictures of her own making, Polaroids of the family and of household items, and colourful cut-outs from magazines. You had to slide the pictures carefully into place over the digital surface. When pressed, each image would set off an audio recording of the corresponding word: it would say 'mom' or 'table' or 'car wash'. It was Ben's voice you heard. He had been more than glad to lend his eight-year-old voice to his little brother.

But it had taken a lot of showing and persuading to get Billy even to touch his Macaw. You'd think the battery had died on him the way he only glanced at it before turning his head to the wall. This is more interesting than the wall, Eve felt like saying. And then, as if he had read her mind, he returned his eyes to the pictures on the device and then gave her a quizzical look.

'Tell us what you want to do, Billy.'

No answer.

Eve asked and Matt asked and Ben asked. And got nowhere fast. Then they tried withholding something, some toy or candy, he'd usually make a hard throaty noise to request, and showed him – over and over – how to request it on his machine. Showed how easy, how much easier than relying on grunts and groans, it was to transmit his exact need or wish. Look, Billy, like this. Like this, see? But he didn't, or maybe it seemed to him the device was harder than going without.

Then one day, no special day, they tried again and he looked at the device differently. It was the same Macaw, the same living room. They said the same things, made the same gestures of explanation. Didn't he want to jump on the trampoline, or to read his books? Choices. Eve had always wanted him to see that the device gave him choices. Jump or read? Now that was a choice. He loved trampolining in the barn, loved his books too – at home as much as in school. He would sit in his chair or on the floor and turn the big, thick pages and look at all the words – he was beginning by now to make them out – and the fantastical illustrations. Their author was one doctor he need never fear – Dr. Seuss.

Billy's face registered interest, understanding.

Eve said, 'What do you want, Billy?'

Matt said, 'What's up, Billy?'

Billy leaned forward and hit a button. 'Book,' Billy said, in Ben's voice.

'Way to go, Billy!'

A tremendous thrill entered him then, and his chair became a rodeo bull. It bucked and rocked him back and forth as he threw out his arms and giggled.

'Here,' said Eve, and her firm hand tamed the chair. 'Here are your books.'

And Billy sat still and turned the pages on his knees and smiled. It was as though he had needed all this time to grow into his big brother's voice.

The technology had been maturing too. Soon he was using a touchscreen capable of expressing not only individual words but also short phrases.

'Excuse me,' the device would help a hungry Billy say. His finger would dart from icon to icon.

'I want.' 'Dictionary.' 'Food.' 'Meat, fish, poultry.' 'Hamburger.'

But none of this progress squared with the uncommunicative boy Billy could be in class. Prone to tantrums. No, not tantrums, Eve would remind his teachers. Not tantrums. A breakdown in communication. In any case, no one in the school had ever seen him use his device.

'Show them,' Eve would tell Billy. 'Show the class what you can do.' No one would believe her if he didn't.

He showed them during one circle time, the children gathered round.

The teacher said, 'What song shall we play today?'

Class favourites included 'The Wheels on the Bus' and 'Old MacDonald'. One of the boys, by the name of Arthur, wanted 'The Ants Go Marching'. This was the umpteenth time this month that the class would hear it. Perhaps Arthur was better at putting his hand up and requesting. Or perhaps the teachers just happened to know all the words to sing along.

Billy dropped his head at the thought of the music starting. *The ants go marching one by one, hurrah, hurrah.*

Music wasn't the problem. He liked music plenty and listened to all sorts of songs: he had an ever-expanding home collection of CDs, he listened to pop and gospel and to Louis

Armstrong. Repetition wasn't it, either. Sure, there were songs in his collection that were good for one listen, but plenty more repaid replaying. He'd simply had enough of this particular song. He'd been patient, he'd listened and listened and now he was all listened out. So he managed to point to his device, left his chair for it, navigated to the page he wanted and clicked a button.

'I don't like this,' said Billy in the device's voice, the nasally synthetic voice that had replaced his brother's.

And with that he navigated back to the homepage and put down his touchscreen, not without a certain flourish, Eve imagined later when the teacher told her.

She knew then she had to keep his machine up to date. You could do that far more straightforwardly than with the Macaw. You could add new icons and the computer would do all the talking. She had to anticipate Billy's appetites, his shifting moods and preferences; she had to adjust to circumstances as they changed. To her son as he changed, sometimes in ways she and her family could not predict.

'It's us,' shouted Eve as she and Matt came through her parents' front door. She was a little out of breath from the evening jog – an expiation for the Yuletide calories – and the house's fireside warmth flushed her cheeks. Returning the keys to her wallet and carrying the smell of chill a step or two towards the living room, she called out, 'Where's Billy?'

'Upstairs with the boys,' Eve heard her father say. The boys being Ben and their cousins.

'He's had his bath,' she heard her mother say. 'I helped him into his pyjamas.'

Eve took off her shoes and went up to see the boys.

Ben was there and the cousins, in the middle of some complicated-looking game, but not Billy. They had figured he was downstairs with nana and papa.

She headed to the bathroom and tried the door and turned on the light. No Billy. She went from room to room but there was no Billy behind the curtains or under the beds or in the closets.

Matt, who had been putting on some coffee, heard the sounds of pacing and fumbling – bedsheets, blankets? – and went up. 'Eve?'

'I can't find Billy.'

He had to be somewhere. She looked unthinkingly in the laundry hamper. Billy's clothes – discarded before his bath – were in there.

They returned to the rooms, hoping against hope that Eve had missed him the first time. Then they went and searched downstairs. The back door in the kitchen was unlocked.

'He's outside,' she shouted.

Her mother called 911. 'Missing child. My grandson. Yes. Nine years old. He's autistic.'

His hand had managed to turn the lock, then pull the door shut behind him – and in his bare feet and pyjamas, his hair damp still from his bath, he had lit out into the dark.

And before she knew it, she was back in her shoes and out the door and running, running as hard as she could. He might be lying in a frozen ditch somewhere, catching hypothermia, and she could never get to him in all this darkness. Not that there were many ditches to fall in, not around these parts, sense and logic might have objected – but they did not object, for the good and simple reason that she had not summoned them. There was no time for that. And the thrust of the thought was valid. Her son was out on his own, God only knew where, in the cold and dark. 'Billy!' she shouted at the parked cars and the stray cats but they did not answer to that name.

There was silence, only silence, and she did not like the sound of it.

On and on she ran through the silent streets and the freezing gloom, glimpsing herself run, some madwoman beside herself with panic, frantic knees up, elbows pumping, going every which way and not a one of them the right. Not minding the risk of ice, or skidding on slushy snow, the nasty fall and the broken wrist or leg or worse she was courting. In her peripheral vision she saw Christmas lights coming on, limning gates and fences and hedges, green and silver and yellow, and just beyond these, on the outermost edges of her mind, she feared she saw something else: a black, frozen and crumpled heap lying somewhere she would never get to.

Then she saw more lights, different these ones, not small and twinkly, they were red and blue and flashing. They were travelling in the direction of her parents' house and slowing as they neared it. Eve ran up to the police car and to the boy in pyjamas on its back seat. He was wet and cold and safe. Someone opened the car door and Billy leapt into her embrace.

He resembled her more than she had known, resembled the boy in *The Snowman* less than he had thought. This was what Billy's aborted flight taught them.

In thirty years Billy has gone through his fair share of devices. These days, he speaks through a Toughbook in tablet mode. Eve tells me it's called that, Toughbook, on account of its resilience; it can survive nasty drops and spills – and Billy. Though, to tell the truth, he's much less hard on his devices than he used to be, his fingers now so accustomed to the pages and icons that you can scarcely keep up.

Eve keeps up. She is in what she might reasonably expect to be the Indian summer of her life, still full of energy, still overtaking men and women half her age on the sidewalk. These people. Move any slower and they'd stop!

'Talk me through Billy's adolescence,' I say.

'Oh boy,' she says. 'Those were bleak years.'

She remembers nights opening her eyes on her disappointingly dark bedroom, only thirty minutes or an hour lighter than the last time she had opened them, and climbing out of bed because she'd hear Billy up and about, thumping his teenage feet the width and length of the corridor. He could continue like that for hours, it seemed, over miles of corridor. How much further before he reached her wits' end? So frazzled, in those instants, she didn't know up from down. Nothing else for it but to wait for the sound of footsteps to recede. Or for sleep to reclaim her first.

He'd started having pain some months before, when he was sixteen, inexpressible, unlocatable pain, and she and Matt had had no rest, taking him to this and that medical department. It might be his wisdom teeth, they had thought. Or his periodic acid reflux. The dentist's X-ray, though, had come up blank, as had the Ear, Nose and Throat man's examinations. The doctors might have hoped Billy's device could tell them where exactly he was hurting. But Billy didn't seem to know where to press or point.

The pain was mysterious. It came and went. When it came

and stayed it could walk him for hours at night along the corridors or in the kitchen.

Who sleeps much anyway? Eve mused on those exhausting nights. (Aside from Matt, the lucky log.) Not babies who wake in raging tears or young lovers in the throes of passion. Certainly not insomniacs or the elderly. Or those with something on their conscience. Maybe, just maybe, there wasn't enough sleep in the world to go round. These night thoughts hardly soothed her then, they only caused her to fall even further behind on her fractured sleep. Forget beauty – her sanity sleep was what she needed. But there was never time. Darned if she remembered the last morning she had pushed snooze.

To think she had once feared a life of boredom.

One morning she woke to marching music – what in hell's name, that marching ants song coming from somewhere in the house. She got up and dressed and crept down the stairs, hearing the music getting louder. It was coming from behind the kitchen's closed door. She opened the door and saw Billy's tall back and his hands up over his ears. The song must be playing on the radio, she thought. And before she could find it to switch it off Billy turned around and sent her a look of exasperation. He dropped his hands from his ears, opened his trembling mouth and hollered, 'I don't like it.'

The alarm woke her.

A dream. She sat up, listened for music in the real house but there was none. It wasn't the first time she had dreamed like this; her brain had plenty of material. More, in fact, since Billy had been taken ill.

Eve threw on her clothes and hastened down the actual stairs to an empty kitchen. He must have gotten peckish in the night – that explained the dirty spoons abandoned beside the sink and the jars left out on the counter, missing dollops of almond butter and blackberry jam. He had always had a good appetite. Ferocious. How he put away a cheeseburger, fries and shake in no time at all.

When he came down for breakfast, she remembered to tell him what reluctance had almost made her forget. She took his device in her hand and showed him the screen and pressed 'hospital'. (The icon consisted of a downloaded photo of the squat concrete building.)

'Hospital,' she repeated.

A frown came on his face. She could hear him thinking, in her translation, Go to the hospital again? I'd better be getting a blueberry muffin out of it. She had had years of practice by then in translating his thoughts.

She explained about their having an appointment next week to see a gastroenterologist. (A new icon to add to her son's device. She pictured twisty, compact tubes at the base of an upper body's outline. Something like that.) She mimed the probing of his tummy. On a sheet of paper she drew the anaesthesia entering his arm until he slept. She told him that his arm might feel warm – that was normal. While he slept, a tiny camera would explore his insides, and he wouldn't feel a thing. Then he would wake up and Mom and Dad would bring him home.

And yes, there'd be his muffin – muffins, even – waiting for him.

The week up, the operation done and the results in (all negative), Eve and Matt were torn between relief and confusion.

If it wasn't his teeth or acid reflux or his digestion, what was it that kept him up some nights pacing like he did? Soon, some nights became nearly every night. Billy paced and paced, driving Eve ever crazier with sleeplessness; she only hoped whatever the cause was it might go away any night now, and then one morning Holly found him on the floor in the kitchen and that was the beginning of the seizures. Shouts. An ambulance. Yet another hospital department.

Thank heavens for Holly, who had been with the Megargels for years, a sitter turned tutor turned all-round assistant – a ball of energy, light of the family's life.

For the seizures and other symptoms the doctors started Billy on unpronounceable tablets with names that seemed to contain far too many x's, y's and z's to be entirely reassuring. Were they necessary? Some days the family could have been forgiven for thinking that perhaps they weren't. He might go to bed and stay there more or less overnight. He might walk up and down the living room in the daytime but that had long been his custom anyway, to pace like that, in the hour before Matt got in from work, while keeping an ear out for the car. He'd hear one approaching and look out the window, then continue pacing when the black Toyota wasn't Dad's red Ford SUV. He seemed just fine then. The same routines. His senses just as sharp. His gaze, for instance, roaming this or that room, would bump up against any misplaced spoon or disturbed photo and he'd set them straight right away.

Other days, however, the returning pain took possession of him and he'd be laid up for hours on end, enduring every secret spasm, enshrouding himself in his blanket. Or else, feeling embattled, attacked by his own body, he attacked it back: he'd suddenly go off and start slapping himself red and raw until the skin broke and wept. Eve and Holly would hold his arms until the rage in him subsided. The face he lifted to the women then was of someone broken, defeated.

Ben called from Michigan, where he was getting a degree in English.

'What's the latest with Billy?'

Eve thought, *He's really sick and nobody seems to know why.* She paused for a steadying breath and said at last, 'He's okay. Could be better. The doctors keep trying him on different meds. He's resting'.

Before long, Thursday nights too he remained in bed. The same Thursday night that went back years. Thursday night was when he and Matt usually sat at the kitchen table picking a restaurant for the weekend. Billy relished the picking, it seemed, at least as much as the future meal – it was always leisurely, methodical. He perused a large menu of restaurant logos which Eve and Matt had inserted into Billy's device over the years. For a while the machine sat silent as Billy scrolled through each logo, lingering over several before pressing the one of his choice. The pizza place, it would seem to be. Matt would give a thumbs up then and wait, knowing what came next. He waited for Billy, already giggling, to switch the page on his screen and tap one of the newer icons, a sentence:

'I changed my mind.'

He might change his mind half a dozen times more before the restaurant's name would be known for certain.

But now the family discontinued their outings to the pizza place (or any other) on the weekend, and soon Billy wouldn't come out even for a doughnut. At mealtimes he barely touched

129

his food, lighter and blander with every month that passed. His skin turned coarse and ashen, his muscles less firm – the once stout calves which he had gotten from all his years of jumping. His tennis shoes sagged in the entryway – little worn and unrecognisably clean, they no longer went on their enthusiastic rampages around the barn, the garden, or up in the air on the trampoline.

In the summer, hot as the Mojave Desert outside, they no longer left for the coast. One time Billy allowed himself to be driven there, but he never left his bed for the beach.

In the winter, between inconclusive hospital tests, Eve sat at the back window that looked out on the garden. Her gaze drifted along the red gnarly bark of the Japanese maple. She saw the insides of her son, those precarious twists and turns in the intimate darkness, like kinked and congested roots; she felt the hard knots of pain that had choked all joy and colour from his body.

Long ago, during the months that she cradled and breastfed Billy, she and Matt had foreseen all kinds of big things for their son. He would ace every school test while raising an army of buddies. He would throw his graduation cap high into a cloudless blue sky. He would write and call home from far-flung lands they'd have a hard time locating on a map. Fall head over heels in love. Marry. Presumably have little Billies of his own.

And recalling every never-would-be scene as she thought of her son's prostrate figure, it was all Eve could do not to succumb to bitterness. Iller boys than Billy talked and put their lives into words, could tell a parent what they were going through; while others, just as mute, had at least their health.

But then she would stop herself because, come on now, such feelings, natural as they were, got her nowhere, they didn't console or give her strength.

Sometimes, feeling very low, she became apprehensive about checking in on him, dreading the strange stillness that met her as she came through his bedroom door. How it unsettled her, that stillness. It was so unlike him, so un-Billy. They were barely on communicating terms by that time, except for those rare moments when he mustered the strength to hold her gaze. Some message passed between them then, something she could word out in her mind. She read in his round blue eyes, 'Yes, I'm listening.' Or, 'No better, the pain is still really bad.'

There he was, laid low and debilitated by his pain, baring his pain to her frightened eyes, his whole being in pain, become pain itself, for it hurt her even to glance at his blanket, or to enter his subdued presence as she neared the bed.

Near or far, at home or out in town, just the thought of him exercised a similarly piercing effect on her. It was something not very far from grief she felt, and shared with Matt.

Their Billy, earthbound. Housebound. Bedridden. Not that it stopped him sometimes – when Eve walked through a room – wrapping his invisible arms around her in a hug.

On other occasions she thought she heard the drums or percussion Billy didn't play any more, and the short-lived relief she felt was that of leaving the eerie silence, since for all his wordlessness Billy had never been silent.

Once, in the early days of his illness, she had gone into the garage just to look at his portable radio. The garage had been converted into a studio for Billy's painting and the radio's accompanying music. On the spattered desk next to the radio (silence did not become it), a brush's bristles parched and stiff; and ahead of the paintbrush, the easel which at this hour her son ought to have been facing. His most recent paintings were propped up against a wall and she looked at them, feverish swirls and dots and splashes made with bubble wrap, rubber spatulas, turkey basters; while on others he had rolled the paint, or flicked and thumbed it over the canvas. They reminded her of something she had noticed as Billy was making them: a gradual narrowing of his palette, relying increasingly on blacks and sombre reds.

She was standing there when she took the call from Michigan and heard Ben ask, 'What's the latest with Billy?' And, looking at the canvases, answered inwardly, 'He's really sick and nobody seems to know why.' She didn't tell him this and he knew from her tone to move the conversation on; he himself had the stress of end-of-term exams not to mention. They understood each other's omissions.

The months of Billy's illness passed, not a day too soon, long months and months amounting inconceivably to years. Aside from Ben's graduation, the occasional anniversary, the Megargels lost track of time. It was during one spring when Eve drove up to New Hampshire, when she parked outside the townhouse she had come to clear, and put a foot through the door, that this realisation struck her. The family's holiday home had become a shrine to the years before the illness. She asked the walls, the dusty furniture, had it really been so long since they last vacationed here? It really had. She learned the date from the magazines on the bedside table, their news long grown old, then ancient.

Over the years of trial and error, little by little doctors came to understand Billy's illness, which was complicated both by its variability and the patient's silence. He was given multiple treatments, for inflammation of the lining in his stomach and of the tube – the oesophagus – that connects the mouth to the stomach, and for the immune system overreaction to this inflammation. Beta blockers were prescribed to calm the pain receptors in his nervous system; too much adrenaline, it turned out, was misleading his body.

Billy was on his fifth or sixth treatment when doctors finally hit on the right combination and dosage. It was a miracle, the slow then sudden change that came over Billy, how he gained weight, muscle, coordination and vigour. He could run again and jump again and laugh and paint and play the drums energetically. He could take up his device as before and swipe the screen and communicate. At night he – and the household – could sleep soundly and wake refreshed. His recovery vindicated his parents' perseverance, their dedication, their faith in him.

In the barn, Eve rolled out her yoga mat, and Billy and the other yogis theirs. The floor seemed even more spacious since the trampoline had settled in a corner.

It was the week before Thanksgiving, and Billy's birthday. His thirty-third birthday. There would be quite the crowd – Ben and his wife, Holly and her wife – around the table.

When Eve first started practising yoga, while Billy was in his teens, she concentrated on her breathing. She breathed out despair and fear and worry; resolve and daring and hope she breathed in. She felt her nerves, like her limbs, grow gradually more supple. Her ability to resist expand.

Now the blood of pride rose to her cheeks as she watched Billy plant his feet firmly in his mat. He looked away from her for an instant, to observe a nonverbal African American friend, who was warming up beside him. The three of them, Eve and Billy and his friend, would agree on every session's poses beforehand on the Toughbook. Most often, like today, they started in mountain pose, drew down their shoulders, lifted their heads, engaged their thighs, and breathed easy.

Yoga was about progress, as Eve's instructor had once said. Stretching a little further, breathing a little easier. Relinquishing, inch by inch, the false comfort of bad posture – and even worse habits of thought. It was about the union of mind and body. It most definitely was not about perfection. Hearing this, Eve had been reminded of a Bible verse, Matthew 5:48, she had often pondered: 'Be perfect, therefore, as your heavenly father is perfect.'

And remembered, too, that the Koine Greek for 'perfect' could be translated differently: 'Be whole . . . as your heavenly father is whole.'

Coming out of the mountain pose, Billy went straight into the tree: he shifted his weight to his right foot, lifted the left by degrees and brought it to his inner right thigh. The small movements were fluent and full of grace. Years of yoga had made him attentive to the language of bodies – how the cocking of a head, the pirouette of a wrist, the minutest shifts in posture can speak louder than words. He could follow what they said. Here in the barn he stood and stretched in his element. The shared air came warmly through his nose and out his mouth. His hips were square, his gaze steady. As he raised his arms skywards – the palms meeting above his head – he kept his balance.

His mother stood back to take in the scene. The way in which she was holding her body, he understood, said everything. Her smile blossomed on his lips.

Amanda

About the accident she would remember very little. Crowds of travelling elbows to dodge. The distraction of public announcements. The rush and rush and rush and then, bam, an unimaginable wall. And then nothing.

She came round to a high-pitched alarm wailing above her head – a remorseless flood of ugly, discordant sound pummelling her eardrums. She became irritated by the commotion it was making. What on earth could have kicked it off? she wanted to say to someone. In all her life she had never heard anything so horrendous.

What she had thought an alarm was in reality her own screams as they broadcast her shock and pain and confusion. She could feel the tiny tremors from feet running in her direction as she lay on the ground. She must have lost consciousness again, because the next thing she knew she was sitting who knew where and being talked to very slowly. She did not recognise the voice – a nurse? a doctor? – and then the realisation of where she was leapt into her mind. The thought flew her hand to her forehead – a long narrow gash above her left eyebrow had needed four stitches. That meant blood. Blood, whatever red looked like, mucking up her face, streaking her jacket. Strewth, she had to be a sight to behold.

And yet she felt unafraid on account of another person in the room, this one familiar. Ah, the sense of Bruce beside her, gentle, reassuring Bruce. She could tell as she listened carefully to his presence that no harm had come to him, as it had to her, though they had been together at the moment of impact.

She listened around, taking in her surroundings. It was a rectangular room with one table in the corner, a small compact table by the sound of it. No windows that she could hear.

Questions from the low, brusque voice – the same or a different one? – she answered incompletely. She could give her name when asked, Amanda Tink, but not her date of birth.

'How old are you?' the stranger asked her and she tried to recollect and said, 'I don't know.' She was too big to be a girl, too smooth-skinned to be middle-aged.

Tears started down her cheeks.

'Don't worry,' said the voice, 'it'll come back to you.' The voice belonged to a man, a medic of some kind. He told her that the blow to her head had left her with a concussion. She'd want to take it easy for a time, put her legs up, lots of rest often being the best medicine. Words to that effect.

But Amanda's attention remained elsewhere. She racked her brains until it came to her. Thirty-seven. She was thirty-seven. Of course she was. A postgrad student at WSU. One brother, a year older; parents, long divorced. Sydney, her home where she formed a couple with Bruce. She had moved to the city, oh, when was it? Her mind meandered between taller and shorter years, dates pictured in flittering dots of Braille: 2007? 2009? 2009.

She wanted to think some more, keep up the remembering,

but a great weariness came over her and she let her head slump to her chest.

It was evening when Amanda and Bruce were led out of the hospital. No sun on their skin, a needling chill in the air, the chill you feel standing too long at an open fridge door, the chill of a late-day breeze in June. Midwinter in their part of the country.

She found the apartment as she had left it but not, in the weeks that followed, its environs. Not the nearby mall, where she had shopped a hundred maybe a thousand times before, and which seemed now to take a perverse pleasure in retreating its stores, withholding them from her – the deli, the chemist's, the supermarket – shuffling them around. What had been a mile return trip became a marathon. To get her bearings, her confidence up, she resorted to playing back in her mind the steps gingerly trodden, the turns taken, the oddly placed poles that turned into people when she approached, men and women standing with their eyes glued to their phones. Once, feeling unequal to the trek, she tried calling a taxi and found it overwhelming. Bruce squeezed her hand extra tight when she told him. The whole intricate business of phoning and explaining and waiting, she said, had made her head swim.

Pills helped some, for the pounding headaches. Shame there were no pills for the piano that played fourth octave B over and over again, and that only she could hear – an unfortunate side-effect that would clear up fast, or else linger on and on, for all the neurologist knew. At the initial consultation the cross-sounding lady behind her keyboard had said, 'Five nine zero three eight.' She meant for Amanda to remember the numbers and recite them back to her.

'Five,' said Amanda. 'Nine.' She could hear the tone of

doubtfulness creeping into her voice. 'Zero,' she continued, less and less persuasively. 'No, eight.' She rubbed her hand over her forehead and felt the Band-Aid above her eyebrow. 'No, sorry, zero'. The right angle of raised dots that pulsed in her mind's eye resembled a zero, she decided, more than it did an eight.

And as she hesitated and stammered, struggling now even to tell a zero from an eight, she thought how easily she would have repeated back all those numbers before. How securely she would have tucked them away in a fold of her mind, just as if she had been doing it all her life. Which, come to think of it, she pretty much had. Telephone numbers and details in books, flight schedules and train times, anniversaries and birthdays. Those of family and classmates and colleagues all coming to her as naturally as her own. Her powers of recall had long been commented on admiringly. The fruit of talent but also of necessity, for where would she have been without them? Someone might come up and greet her in the street and she would instantly put a name to the voice. A conference on disability advocacy might ask her to speak at a moment's notice and she would have every fact and figure published in its pamphlet, and those not published in it, at her fingertips. And all thanks to the same powers that had long ago taken her out of Rochedale, a little suburb south of Brisbane, to study media at university, and from university into the office of People with Disability Australia, 750 kilometres away, in Sydney.

That had surprised precisely no one in her circle, knowing how she had always intended to go far. Distance had never held any fear for her, nor the ever-changing space around her body that her senses probed. Good as a guide dog when it came to finding her way around a park, out of a building or across a busy road. No longer. Now, such recollections of her past self were like the memories of some other person.

At least she was happy, more than happy, to lie down and rest just as she had been advised. Indeed, she slept like nobody's business. Only after the first ten days had passed, in one immense blur, did she begin again to tell day from night. She slept at night with a warm blanket, slept soundly, but she did not dream. She would wake and feel lonely for her dreams, because they had always offered her good company. Then one night she had a dream that had often visited her. She dreamed she was going along the avenue that was close to her apartment. She was not walking, she was hovering or flying several storeys above the footpath. It was simple for her to sense and hear where the buildings stood as she glided near and past them, as simple as in her waking life, her walking life, each surface – glass and brick and concrete – disclosing its characteristic sound. No matter if people far below her impatiently shoved, or thoughtlessly blocked the path. No matter if she didn't have her cane. The freedom. That was the feeling that stayed with her after waking, and which she would try each time to smuggle into the day ahead.

'Sure you're ready?' Bruce said when she announced she had to be getting back to the university. She had wakened and felt by the Braille calendar on her desk that it was the beginning of winter semester 2015.

'Ready as I'll ever be.' As a matter of fact, Amanda felt nowhere near ready. She was talking to him on the phone (their apartments were minutes away by foot). She couldn't have got the words out in his presence.

'It's only been a month.'

She knew that. But there could be no question of letting

her studies slide. Enrolling six months earlier for a Master of Research had been a huge decision; going back inside a classroom after nearly ten years. During her degree she would investigate the influence of disability on literary production.

'I will figure this out.'

Day by day, she was gathering her strength, adapting – recovering was not a word she would use to describe the process her mind and body were embarking on. The apartment smelled of coffee. She made herself notes – prompts in Braille – for everything. How to compose an essay, how to send email, how to get a taxi to the university's front steps.

'Nothing is easy,' she said to Bruce, in a subsequent call. 'Everything takes twice as long as it used to do. But I'm learning. I'm learning so much.'

She had no idea then that she had a whole thesis inside her.

'This work is only possible because of who the former Amanda was,' she would write in a commentary on her first assignment after returning to class. 'But she was always so hard on herself. I feel like she made me the one most likely to succeed with a brain injury. She always had a keen interest in how brains work; she was the most organised person in the world; and she acted on her passion in the nick of time.'

The days were long and warm and welcoming. This was June, the first in Paris since the pandemic, and my American friends, John and Mary, had emailed to say they were in town. Spry and pushing seventy – age to them was only a number – they'd been sightseeing all day before reaching the bistro where we'd given each other rendezvous. They brought a gift – a set of illustrated postcards showing their native birds: chestnut-backed chicka-dees and dark-eyed juncos – as well as an acquaintance of theirs up from her home in southern France. She was a freshly retired Australian, spry herself, with whom conversation came easily. She had a connection with books, my friends reported, an occasional hand in literary festivals, which perhaps explained their bringing her along to meet me.

Halfway through our meal I finally asked the question I had been saving up for her from the start, one I always asked on the rare occasion that I met an Australian: 'Have you read Les Murray?' She put down her fork at the poet's name. 'Absolutely. He came to read at our international festival.' That had been in Shanghai a few years before his death in 2019, at the age of eighty. 'He came right over to me,' she said. 'He had something he wanted to tell me. Do you know the first thing he said? He said, "Michelle, I'm autistic."'

So she had sensed the reason for my question which was a deeply personal one. Les Murray and I went back a long way. I had read him in my twenties, corresponded with him and translated his work for a French volume in my thirties, eulogised him on turning forty. He had been a mentor to me: an oft-cited contender for the Nobel Prize whose writing was transparently, gloriously neurodivergent.

Thinking this, I looked at Michelle and John and Mary and wondered how to continue. The word autistic had meanings other than the ones they understood. Not far from this bistro, I said, Murray and I had shared the stage at an international writers' conference in 2015. We had sat gazing out at the hall-sized dusk to which we took turns reading: Murray, his poems; I, my adaptation of them into French. This was our first – and as it proved our only – in-person encounter, and it goes without saying that I was somewhat awed. Yet I had no nerves, no stage fright. We shared an instant understanding. The years and kilometres that normally separated us disappeared. And all of this we put into words, shapely and savoury, delighting in them – Australian English and French ones. We read. We conversed. We rhymed.

The poet's name, I told my friends at dinner, had given my Parisian publisher some trouble, or at least pause for thought. The publisher had wanted to put 'Leslie Murray' on the cover of my translation, fearing readers might get the wrong idea otherwise. And it was true, there were two ways of reading 'Les Murray' in French. It could also be read as 'The Murrays'. Which, as it happened, seemed rather fitting for a poet so large, who contained multitudes.

'But understandably his agent would not hear of it, so Les it was.'

Our waitress was collecting the plates, and after we had finished complimenting the food and choosing dessert, my friends turned the conversation to my British background. They always loved asking about that, loved hearing about my cockney father and my bookish mother and the red double-decker I would ride to and from school (where I began to learn my French). My other school, I liked to say, was the London council house that I called home in those days, buzzing and full of play and chat with eight sisters and brothers.

Here I stopped and waited, for people usually exclaimed in surprise at the number of my siblings. Instead, Michelle said, 'Nine children? You're the eldest? Well, how about that, I'm also the eldest of nine.' And then she asked out of the blue, 'What's your birthday?'

'January,' I said, 'January thirty-first.'

A look of astonishment spread across her face. 'Me too.'

The odds of our crossing paths had to be extravagant. If I had read the scene in a book, I wouldn't have believed it. I felt dazed and yet curiously revitalised by the idea that life is full of accidents.

And there was another reason for my feeling as I did. Another coincidence that only enlarged my sense of wonder. Not very long before my chance meeting with Michelle in Paris, I received a message all the way from Sydney. The sender had reached me through my author website: 'My name is Amanda Tink, and I am finishing a PhD thesis on the influence of autism on Les Murray's writing. My argument, from the position of a blind autistic Australian, is that its influence was profound and that Murray's identifying as autistic, even though most critics refused to engage with it, makes him our earliest-known autistic published author.'

She invited me to read a draft of her thesis. I emailed back enthusiastically. Several exchanges later, Amanda (as she signed off by then) sent it over in an attachment, and when I clicked it open and went from one page to the next, I met thoughts and insights on Murray's work that I had never found elsewhere. I underlined many passages and told her as much. One email led to another and we were soon in regular contact. Sometimes, we wrote, other times we called. With time our conversation expanded to include more personal topics. She told me how windows emit a particular sound and so did doors and tables, lamps and bookshelves. Even half a bottle of wine, whose sound was distinct from a full bottle's. She explained it like this: for sighted people, a room is filled with light. Every item, feature, piece of furniture is a different reflection of this light. A white door looks different to a long desk or a thick wall because each reflects the light in its own way. Now, for her, a room is filled not with light but sound. Sound, bouncing constantly back and forth, much as sighted people's light, is a reflection of everything that surrounds her.

She told me also how, growing up, she often confounded people, blind and sighted alike – they never knew quite what to make of her. The sensation was always mutual. She talked of schooldays, of learning to read by touch, of loving the rub of certain words as she pressed her fingers to the Braille letters. Her years working in disability awareness. The smells and sounds of Sydney. The return to uni on a scholarship. Her brain injury. Her own special encounter with the poet.

In this way, I began to picture every scene just as Amanda described it to me, using research and my imagination to fill in any gaps.

Beneath the date, Tuesday, 23 May 2017, the poster had said 5 p.m. But people were already coming through the door shortly after four o'clock, enquiring whether they were in the right place. 'The Woolley Building,' they said, 'lecture theatre N395,' they said, as though it were some sort of a riddle.

'Just here,' the event organiser said, pointing at a door crowned by a red-brick arch. 'But you'll have to come back in a bit. We're not open yet.' Maybe watches running fast, he thought as he showed them back out. If any students still wear watches. Or perhaps they were regulars come to claim the best seats. He hadn't been with the University of Sydney long enough to recognise them if they were.

While he was wondering about this, another person had

arrived. A blind student with short-cropped hair who followed his cane towards the brick arch. 'We're not open yet,' the organiser called out hastily. G'day, he was about to say to him then, to offset the sharpness, before checking himself. It wasn't a him. The hair, he thought. That would be the hair's doing. Then he almost said to the student, You right there?, imagining her lost. But of course she was not lost. Not at all.

'Les Murray,' she said. 'I'm here for the reading.' He led her along the white-painted corridor and deposited her on a bench. The same bench to which, some minutes later, he escorted the poet. The old knees playing him up, apparently. All the way down from Bunyah. But at least he had got down here in one piece and that was the main thing. The student and the poet started talking and he left them to their discussion.

More people wanted to enter now, angling to break in on the conversation with the student. Staff from the English and Lit departments, going by their shoes and jackets. Their classes, too, with the poet's books, quite a few of them read ragged.

Not a bad turnout for a poet. Not shabby at all.

At ten to the organiser opened the door.

The blind student got up and the poet gave her an arm into the hall.

'So,' said Bruce. His voice was smiling. 'How was it?'

He and Amanda were sitting in the kitchen of his apartment, at coffee o'clock (late morning, to me or you). The mugs on the table warmed their hands, and she heard him push her favourite chocolate biscuits towards her.

Bruce wasn't just her partner, he was her, well, most other things. He had become her memory for appointments, and class deadlines too, occasionally her alarm call on the mornings she overslept, always her assignments' first reader (after the computer program which read aloud every word as she typed). He read her work in Braille, sometimes putting an apologetic finger on a typo – the fault of the word processor far more often than Amanda.

They had met on an Internet mailing list for the blind, back when Internet mailing lists were a thing.

'Yummy,' she said. 'The biscuit, I mean.'

She was still pinching herself. Murray's reading had very nearly passed her by. She had learned about it by chance thanks to a last-minute email. Afterwards she had returned to her flat quite a lot later than planned. It had taken her half this morning – like every morning since the concussion – simply to collect her thoughts – to piece together who she was, where she had been, what she had been doing, and with whom. Half-hour by half-hour, with mounting excitement and disbelief, it had all come back to her. The sheer luck and joy and delight of it.

She was getting round now to telling him what, not an hour earlier, she had told herself, 'I met Les! Oh, you should have been there, Bruce, you should have heard him.'

When she was dropped at the place – it was on the campus of the poet's alma mater – someone had directed her to a bench, and whom had she found waiting to go inside but Murray himself. No, hang on, he had joined her on the bench. That was it. She had heard his voice nearing as it spoke to the same someone. Felt the bench absorb a second weight. The two of them, Amanda and the poet, side by side.

She was speaking more rapidly than usual. Excitement had

that effect on her. Perhaps, as well, because she had plenty to recount.

'One second,' said Bruce. 'You found yourself side by side with the subject of your thesis?'

'Glad I'm making sense,' said Amanda.

'And what did you say to him?'

'Well, hi, for starters.'

She hadn't felt tongue-tied in his presence. She'd been so forward as to introduce herself. Listened to herself telling him about the thesis, not as straightforwardly as she might have hoped – that had been the adrenaline talking. Aspects of autistic thought are especially conducive to creativity, she'd said, notably literary creation. Inventing and playing with words; speaking – or writing – at length on a favoured topic; revelling in rhyme and the repetition of sounds; listing, arranging, classifying.

A thing she'd always loved about Murray's poetry was the layers, the rich delineation of his characters' worlds slowing the pace of each text, inviting the neurotypical reader to experience all the fine detail and resulting sparks of idea and memory that autistic perception provides. She had in mind his emu poem, as she called it, the poet's ode to an emu. In this work, which she'd spend many pages of her thesis analysing, the curious, omnivorous, remarkable bird becomes autism's defiant emblem.

Early days, she'd said, though her project already had a title: 'Never Towing a Line: Les Murray, Autism and Australian Literature'.

When she'd finished speaking, he'd made a low guttural sound in his throat. The sound had been warm, encouraging, conspiratorial. This young woman's going to get a lot of academics' backs up, the sound had said, and good for her. He'd said nothing else just then. He hadn't needed to.

Bruce was about to ask if he had been the same in person as he was on the page. But he did not get the sentence out before she said definitely, he was, is.

'Call it an autistic energy,' she said. The same watchfulness that she found in his poems; the same restraint. Wanting to reach out, but doubting it'll be worth his effort, since his effort would need to be so much greater than most other people's. She knew the feeling only too well.

How long had she had the poet to herself? A quarter of an hour, it would have been. An opening exchange between them and then ... She tried to remember precisely. And then. And then, something like a crackle. A faint crackle around Murray, like static, telling her he required a moment to himself, the peace of this little corridor. Not that she had minded. Amanda, who was versed in sharing silences, leaned back and obliged.

She was not, in ordinary circumstances, much of a talker herself. She recalled all the years she had spent with her brother, blind from birth as she was, but also non-speaking. His silence had never been oppressive, but accommodating. She had always felt at home with him.

And anyway, you couldn't expect to get much more out of Murray just then, she thought, not before the reading. Not a question of nerves; it wasn't that, more an adjustment. A moment to absent himself from the proceedings, retreat into a corner of his mind and return readied. Amanda could detect the difference when the crackle left him. He was present again. Serene. They were minutes now from going in and the reading starting.

Amanda let another minute pass and then she said quietly, 'It's always been my experience that what we do with our minds, we do with our whole bodies.'

Murray said, 'Definitely.'

'I almost forgot,' she said to Bruce. 'Someone took a photo of me with Les. I heard a click and felt the flash. Lucky thing I'd dressed up for the occasion.'

She had heard people advise sitting absolutely still for photos, even stiller than she would have been sitting then, or else smiling to show all your teeth, or perhaps both at the same time. She had also heard it said to stay natural and to be yourself, whatever that was supposed to mean. The somewhat peevish tone in which all this advice had been given out had made her think that photography must be something particularly complicated, capricious, even treacherous.

She wondered what it was the photographer had thought to record of them in that moment. Something for the snapper to show later to family and friends, a souvenir of the evening. A 'sweet picture' as it might be called, of two peas in a pod, two originals.

The companionable silence between them had continued for another splendid minute or two. It had been broken only by the new arrivals, eager for the poet to sign their books. 'To Peter, please, Les.' 'For Susan, happy retirement.'

Suddenly, the poet was getting up.

'May I?' Murray had said to her.

She said he might.

Take her arm, and lead her in towards her seat.

Something else, after thinking of her brother, had surfaced in Amanda. Another scene from her childhood.

Nippy out. The wind, when it blows hard, as cold as could

be. Brittle, crackling leaves carpet the ground. They crunch underfoot. Towards the tail end of a Queensland autumn, this would be, late in May.

At that time of year grown men might still go about in shorts, in denial of the cold. To hear them talk you'd think they have only mislaid the summer. They leave out the mozzies when they speak like this, and the heat that made them sweat buckets; the temperatures that drew instant converts to the cool shade of a church.

Amanda doesn't miss the heat; she never could stand it. Never missed pushing back the fringe of perspiration she grows along her brow. Nor summer's awful stickiness. All those tacky Christmas beetles that seem to make a beeline – a beetle line – for her.

She is in high school, not long there, but already she knows her way around. It is lunchtime and she is walking through the grounds, and dressed for them in a jumper. She is with her teacher, the rare one who seems to understand her, though he is sighted.

'Let me have a word with the principal about your books,' he says. He is considerate that way. Her textbooks in Braille are strewn with misprints, she has discovered, or else impart information that is long out of date.

They are passing by the outdoor swimming pool, which has lately been drained and cleaned for repairs.

She asks about the pool: would it not be interesting to go in while it is empty, but full of sound, and the teacher says he has never thought of that – a pool of sound – but it could be arranged.

He never says her thoughts are odd or weird or batty, as others do.

A day or two – that is all the time he needs to make the arrangements. The key to the pool gate turns once, twice, and he lets her in.

The pool steps bring her down into a long wide space that goes on and on in a rectangle. A compact volume of air has replaced the buoyant water and she ventures into the sound waves, leaning against a wall as the floor slopes towards the deep end. She advances slowly, because of the slope, and she prefers to take her time, anyway, to explore. The wall, her hand notices, has an agreeable give to it, the surface both firm and springy. These walls grow with every step she takes – where she is standing, the absent water would already be shoulder-high.

'How are you going down there?' asks the teacher, standing poolside.

'Good,' she says. She listens around her, not to the litter of leaves but to the falling notes her heels make, and the further down she goes the more the air seems to thicken as the walls exhale a smell of chlorine. When she reaches the deep end and hears her muffled steps come to a halt, an eddy of indecision catches her leg, but she shakes it free. She is more curious about the pool than she is anxious of slipping on its floor, so she lets go of the wall now and crosses every would-be lane.

She will get herself out of breath walking widths, and then lengths.

The teacher is patient and lets her be.

Minutes after meeting the poet, there she sat in the first row, the deep end of a packed lecture theatre. The closed door refusing admission to draughts. Murray, who had taken his place at the carpeted front, was holding his book close to his mouth as he read aloud, the words softening as they passed through the pages. At that moment, everyone was listening to 'It Allows a Portrait in Line Scan at Fifteen'.

'Sounds familiar,' said Bruce in his kitchen.

He was back up at the coffee machine for a refill. Such an intriguing title for a poem, one closest to Amanda's heart. Murray, the autistic father, paying homage to his teenage autistic son. (The son would have to be in his forties by now.) Bruce listened now as Amanda recited it from her Braille notes. As she read the lines in which the father admires his son's progress, and the son, contemplating the future, says, *I gotta get smart*, Bruce thought he heard her voice quiver. That closing line, she said afterwards, her voice recovered and gently self-mocking. It never failed to get her.

It moved her in the hall too, the night before, though she had heard it more times than she could dare to count. Around a year ago she had tracked down a recording of Murray on stage in Paris and in it he recites this very poem – all four minutes and four seconds of it (counting the six seconds of applause before the video cuts out). She caught herself comparing the two versions, the recording she knew so well and this live reading, while she listened. She was pleased with what she heard and not surprised. The Murrays were the same in Paris as in front of her, putting on the same accents – now the father's, now the son's – and accentuating the same words. So that the differences, subtle as they were, in timing and in intonation, produced in her a thicker, richer, layered sound.

The acoustics in the hall were as good as she could have hoped for. From where she sat, Murray's voice came over loud and close and warm. After listening to every poem, as the poet paged through his book, or helped himself to a glass of water, Amanda let her ears travel the hall, hearing how high the ceiling rose and how far up behind her the rest of the audience's seats climbed. Along the wall that ran parallel to the street, she could pick out pairs of curtains, heavy and long and there, she surmised, to keep in the heat and keep out the gaze of any passers-by.

Creak, creak, creak went the hall's rows of wooden seats – sounding their age – as the occupants shifted their weight between poems.

But whenever Murray cleared his throat and began again, she never took her ears off him.

He would read eleven poems that evening – Amanda tapped the title of each in turn on her Braille note-taker; she couldn't trust her short-term memory with them, or with much else, for that matter.

Long gone was the woman who had flown regularly on her own as far as San Francisco (the conference hotel's rooms, she remembered, had all been numbered in Braille), the woman who thought of everything, who never had enough hours in a day. Two years on, the side-effects of her concussion still lingered. Probably they were permanent. Doctors could not fully explain it, but then again all her life there'd been plenty about her that doctors could not explain. She found that rather reassuring.

And the effects had not been all bad. There was something to be said for letting go. When she thought of her life now it was without any weight of expectation, and she knew to make the most of every instant. Just to take a taxi out and feel herself in motion. To leave herself in chance's charge for an hour or more. Just to sit in a lecture hall, all ears, taking each line of poetry as it came.

Her flying days were over, but this did not mean that the world could not come to her. The suburbs of Brisbane, where her parents still lived, sometimes came to her. And now, on this surprise visit, the poet's rural Bunyah. The Bunyah of bush and paddocks and cattle tracks.

When Amanda began at WSU, her professor had read to the class some bush ballads. Not any by Murray but some compulsory Henry Lawson. It was Lawson who would give Amanda the idea for her thesis, though he had died in 1922. Lawson, she learned, had lost his hearing to an ear infection in a boyhood without antibiotics. His deafness, to read Lawson tell it, had driven him into himself and made a writer of him. But this story was little known outside of disability studies; generations of Australians were unaware that the verses they grew up reciting had been composed by a deaf man. It made Amanda wonder which other authors had had their invisible differences erased, smoothed over, ironed out. A whole side of their life's work silenced. This thought would keep coming back to her, until the day she read Murray and knew at once that she would write about him. Because, in his own way, over forty years, from various angles, he had been writing about her.

An emu's 'alert periscope' and a bat in a cave – to Murray, a 'tufty, crinkled ear' – could receive all of her attention; likewise his whales who 'sing into sight'. Who 'peer in long low tones . . . to river-tasting and oil-tasting coasts'. She was moved by a gum tree's leaves in windy autumn, 'swapping pace and place in an all-over sway'. As she was by the poet's admission that his awkward body never danced, save for his hands 'on bits of paper'.

Naturally it wasn't all plain reading. Some of the poems had a reputation for being difficult. Certain words might trip up her fingers, cause them to backtrack. Words that were never meant for her (or so people might think) – Gaelic, Aboriginal, colours. But she remained unperturbed. Foreign words she could check in a dictionary. 'Feallsanachd' is philosophy. 'Gnamma' is a desert rock hole. 'Yellow' – which sounds and spells like something out of a native Australian language – is warm like the sun, she knows. Fluffy and honey-smelling like the golden wattle. Happy – quite a few sighted people say – 'a happy colour'. Loud, say others – 'that T-shirt is loud'. Having been raised by sighted parents, in a sighted society, Amanda has absorbed all this and more. Absorbed that ripe – but not unripe or overripe – bananas come in the same colour – unlike apples. That mixing yellow paint and blue makes green. That the night confers near-invisibility on black cats. That colours in poems can be read in multiple ways.

So many marvellous lines the poet recited that evening in the hall, alternately moving and slyly humorous, inviting tears, then laughter, and answered with each.

A bittersweet nostalgia was conveyed in the lines Murray recited to close the reading. Sydney in the fifties. The poet as a fresher from the sticks.

'When Two Percent Were Students'
Gorgeous expansion of life

all day at the university,
then home to be late for meals,
an impractical, unwanted boarder . . .

She hadn't planned to stick around once the reading was over. She would make straight for the door, flag down a taxi on the street and get herself home, still full of the poet's words. But where on earth were all the taxis when you needed one? While she was waiting with arm outstretched, the reading's organisers and their guest had followed her out and asked her along to dinner.

'That's one invitation I can't refuse,' she had said, after a moment's hesitation, doing her best to keep the nerves out of her voice, since she hardly ever stayed out these days. Indeed, it seemed to her like forever since she had last gone and sat in a restaurant.

Not far to go, luckily. Someone had opened the door and she could hear the drinkers and diners inside, their hubbub as echoes of walls, tables and bottles. She fastened her ears on these, the better to navigate the room, as she entered and let the commotion engulf her.

Amanda could tell from the way the voices at her table gave their orders that they were all seasoned restaurant-goers.

She could scarcely distinguish the voices that addressed her. Nor easily reply to anyone. Words disappeared in the general clamour so that you had to lean in and raise your voice to be heard.

The men (they were all men) had made an effort to include the poet. They had repeated themselves. Yelled, 'Come again?' when he failed to speak over the restaurant noise. But his gruff voice would not carry, and in a short time the men retreated to their plates, so that the table divided into two groups, two atmospheres: the men on one side, Murray and Amanda on the other. One side shouting talk and the other staying silent. Not a good silence, Amanda felt, or, at least, not one that was altogether comfortable. Not like the silence they had shared just before the reading. She sensed a desire on the poet's part to speak, now that the reading was over and he had some food inside him. 'Nice hall for it, I thought, good sound, don't you reckon?' she imagined him saying. If only everyone and their raucous cousin in here would let him get a word in edgewise. The place was getting so loud that she could barely hear herself think. Fortunately, that wasn't her habit, to hear herself think. Rather she felt her thoughts and the words they formed prickle inside her.

He wouldn't ask her what she had made of the reading. He wouldn't ask her when he knew already.

When they had put the poet in a taxi, and shouted hoarse farewells, one of the men said to the others, 'Perhaps he'd've rathered gone somewhere less noisy, Les.'

Amanda repeated to Bruce what the man had said about Murray: 'He looked really crook.'

At first she thought she must have misunderstood, but she heard the others chiming in, saying, 'Yeah, poor bloke, didn't look well, did he?'

'He is getting on. In his seventies.'

'Put on even more weight.'

But the poems, thought Amanda. The hour's worth of poems. All those words that opened rooms within rooms within rooms inside you. Words that took your mind in at least five different directions at once.

She wished the men would say, 'I loved the line about . . .' but they said nothing like it.

The longer they had talked, the older and balder and fatter

and sicker a man they turned the poet into, the higher she could feel her temper rise.

What had the poet's old man looks to do with anything? He hadn't come for a medical, or to rouse anyone's pity.

'Poor Les,' they had said.

'Poor Les yourself,' she had felt like saying back.

'What are youse on about, I wanted to say, it's completely beside the point. Should I have done?' she said to Bruce, who had been rinsing their mugs in the sink.

'No, they wouldn't have got it.'

That had been her thought too. They would only have gone silent on her and paid no notice. And anyway, she had remembered then their kindness to invite her along like that and felt better disposed towards them.

And it was not like any of their remarks had been news to her. She had read such a portrait in Murray's own self-deprecating words, part of his recent output. But she disliked them coming from anyone else.

The simple truth was, she had never much cared for appearances. A person's looks – pretty or ugly or pretty ugly – being neither here nor there. Only once or twice, in her teens and twenties, had she bothered with make-up or clothes thought fashionable in imitation of sighted people (and some blind she knew), and neither experiment had lasted very long.

She remembered, from back in primary and high school, sighted girls feuding pointlessly over their favourite heart-throbs. 'He's five foot eight,' a girl would say of this or that screen or pop star. 'He's so not,' another would retort, 'more like five foot seven and a half.'

She'd remembered this in the taxi home from the reading. It had made her laugh.

Amanda

*

Woolloongabba. Not a word Amanda could ever forget, even now. She had started school – a school for the blind – there. Twenty minutes or so in the taxi from her parents' home.

Her mother had worked in an office as a typist. Her father sold automobile spare parts, and would later give tours of Brisbane on his motorcycle.

Woolloongabba. In her memory were the tricycles, the breathless circling of the schoolyard. Round and round and round you went until the air inhaled blazed the lungs. Or you fell off. Then a grown-up would come and pick you up and kiss the graze or scrape better. 'Haven't you been in the wars, Amanda?'

No helmets in those days. No protection pads for elbows and knees. She'd assent to the kiss but not to being picked up. She'd pick herself up. Then jump back in the saddle. How hard and fast she'd pedal! Tutting at the walls – a click, click, click of the tongue – so as to hear the bricks as they approached, and know just when to turn.

The first time she had laid fingers on a page of Braille was in year one. She was six and making the acquaintance of a machine called the Perkins Brailler, a sort of typewriter, though the keys were few, in a single row, and wrote dots that embossed the paper. 'A' was a single raised dot you typed with your left index. 'C' – two dots – required both indexes to depress their keys simultaneously. You typed the four dots of 'G' with the index and middle finger of both hands. When she typed ('brailled') a sentence, a ding told her she had seven spaces left before she reached the margin. Then she counted to seven as she typed, pressed the new line button, moved the cursor back, and continued writing.

The Perkins used sheets of paper that were rather thick and stiff. Amanda would pull hers out of the machine when she was done, lay it flat and get a feel for reading. She trailed her left index along each sentence, felt the tiny bumps of its words and the tingles flashing up her spine. Soon, whenever she spoke a sentence, she found she could summon up every dot of every word and sense them in her mind: the repeating diagonals in 'taxi', the vertical drops in 'ball', the expansive texture in 'book'.

Around this time, education policy in Queensland was changing; disabled pupils were being integrated into mainstream schools, and Amanda joined them reluctantly. It was hard to leave her class of half a dozen in Woolloongabba for a class of thirty. Obtaining good grades did not make it any easier. She never got used to the ways of these bigger schools and pursued her own curriculum on the side.

Now that she was a full-fledged reader, she needed a supply of books; but books in Braille occupied only a modest shelf of the school library, a poor excuse for a library really. There were some novels that she could check out, but no poetry. An abridged biography of Louis Braille. For the rest, textbooks. She did open their covers, during playtime, and it was then that she learned to what tuneless uses language might be put. All the same she read on, the pages at least making up in interesting words what they lacked in story. At home, her hands wandered inside the longest of these tomes for hours. History. Geography. Physics. Music. She read until her fingers ached and she stopped to rub them. She was gathering words, much as other children gather insects or stickers. She could make a game of locating those with similar feels, vowels in common, palindromes. Those that go well together in a sentence. Sentences which, spoken aloud, play a melody of strength or wariness or pleasure. A great inquisitive itch urged this compiling and listing and sorting, and it would never entirely leave her. She was discovering how a word, used right, becomes an echo – an echo of the world.

She felt her mind encompass new possibilities, among them, the possibility of belonging.

Always, as she grew up, Amanda sought out little oases of silence – what other people think of as silence – in a library, or at her brother's side. Away from these she was seldom out of the oppressive sound of talk and traffic and television. Even long after she went to bed, her parents' house would not fall quiet. The TV set, unplugged and two rooms down, kept up its pestering whine. On summer nights, cooling walls popped and creaked; year-round, water gurgled in pipes. Noises that lit up her brain, and held her back from sleep. A Walkman. That was the solution she came up with. An audiobook on cassette – the volume upped just enough to block out the bedroom. Some nights, for a change, she switched on the radio – through which she would go on to discover just how magical poetry could be.

It might have been during the day, not at night. She had got into the habit of listening to the radio after class. One day, then, she had come into her room and turned the dial on her Walkman. Emily Dickinson was on. Emily Dickinson on ABC national radio.

This would have been the mid-nineties. She was eighteen then, starting out on her bachelor's degree in media.

The name pronounced on the radio meant nothing to Amanda, other than an invitation to listen. She was ever eager to learn something new. As she sat and listened, the realisation crept up on her that the lady talking rather slowly, even strangely, was not in fact talking but reciting, and that she was not Emily Dickinson. The broadcaster was reciting something like a nursery rhyme but it wasn't quite that. It was more solemn. Longer words. Latin-sounding. Like something a sorcerer might say, Amanda thought. *Higitus figitus.* It made her think of an incantation.

At the end of the programme, a discussion of Dickinson's life and work, the broadcaster would have said 'poet'. *That was a reading of selected verses by the American poet Emily Dickinson,* the lady might have said.

Amanda went to her computer at the university the next day and looked the poet up. She downloaded some Emily Dickinson.

She would download more poets after that. But not Murray. Not yet. That would be for another, later, time. Another her.

It is a hot day, a yellow day, and the emu stops to drink the morning's shower at a rock-hole. Her neck is long and thin and curved to Amanda's touch. Circuitous must be the raindrops' journey through it. When the beak lifts at last, Amanda follows her across the pages and kilometres, in and out of the shade of the kurrajong trees, tasting dust. The bird is gawky and shy. She does not sing as she zigzags, though she wears her hair like a Beatle. (That is what the Braille says.) Her attention goes to pebbles, big and small, round and oval, smooth and jagged, and all of them, appetising. Pebbles that, closer to towns, are in fact bottle tops. Collectibles in the private museum of her stomach.

Amanda knows all this from her reading, in particular the

poem by Les Murray whose full title is 'Second Essay on Interest: The Emu'.

She knows the shape of the bird's body, from the head to the three toes, thanks to a scale model she bought online several years ago.

The model stands on her computer desk. The emu poem lies at the heart of her thesis.

She takes time out to keep coming back to these lines – to this sun and rock and tracks in the sand.

The roaming freedom of an emu.

Cédric

'Monsieur Villani, Cédric Patrice Thierry, has voted.'

The woman's voice was neutral. It was her election official's duty to pronounce each voter's name as they slid their envelope into the ballot box. The rangy man at the box was none other than the district's deputy in the National Assembly; after a short campaign, he hoped to secure a second five-year term. This scene in which the woman and deputy were taking part, in a classroom in the Essonne, outside of Paris, was being filmed for TV, and during those self-conscious seconds the man saw himself in the mirror of the camera's gaze: his pageboy brown hair and three-week-long beard. A glittering spider brooch on his lapel. A shirt, its collar open.

Viewers, turning to the day's rolling news (or to one of the bulletins), had long ceased to be captured by the spider. In any other country, of course, or here as well ten or twelve years ago, that's just about all anyone *would* see; only, people in France had grown so accustomed to the sight by June 2022 they could take it more or less for granted.

Cédric Villani's unique style. Many had discovered it on late-night culture shows; many more, in primetime interview slots. I'd seen it in both and also on the news – long before his foray into politics – in 2010 when he won a Fields Medal, among the most prestigious prizes in mathematics. Say 'Cédric Villani' thereafter and you pictured his three-piece suit completed by a silk cravat – red, green, blue or white – a pocket watch, and the eight-legged brooch that intrigued so.

What planet are you from? the interviewers and presenters asked him, or wished to, jokingly or half-jokingly. From what century?

But it was simply his style, he noted quietly, not speaking in jest. The spider? Well, it came out of a personal collection of several dozen. It was a mystery why he wore these brooches. However hard questioners tried pressing him he always denied them any explanation.

The impression left by these media appearances in his life before politics had been of unabashed eccentricity; but also, and inseparable from this, of a restless intelligence employed in furiously obscure ways. All those evenings, not long after suppertime, he had come into millions of homes and spoken in that soft and reedy voice of his about excited plasmas and lazy gases, curved spaces and differing geometries and the surprising harmonies in a theorem. He was happiest, most fluent, describing the beauty he detected in these harmonies. The remembered joy would animate his body and widen his large brown eyes and sometimes, as he was speaking, he rocked himself ever so gently back and forth.

His voice had seemed – after a period of getting used to it – innocent: it seemed to say things as they were, without distortion. The verbal tics and tricks that infect so much of public speech were, in him, nowhere to be heard. Each of his utterances rang with sincerity.

Cédric

In the autumn of 2012, around the time of the release of my third book, I was invited to address a multidisciplinary conference on society in the future. It was taking place before a large audience at L'Olympia, the capital's oldest concert hall. Bryan Adams had played there a few weeks before, and the Pixies – not the easiest acts to follow.

One of the organisers led me backstage to a large dressing room and I stepped inside, expectant. I was early and most of the other speakers due to go on hadn't arrived yet. As I went to hang up my coat I noticed a pair of feet in socks lying on the floor over by the far wall. The owner of these feet, hearing the clatter made by the coat hangers, promptly stirred and rose and came over to greet me. He'd been lying on his back to collect his thoughts, he said. He didn't need to introduce himself.

A freedom of limb, a face shaven clean (as it always was in those years), a spontaneity in his speech. At once he addressed me familiarly as *tu*, perhaps because he had read my work or seen me on stage or TV somewhere before, or because we were rather close in age, both of us in our thirties, or quite simply because he wasn't one to stand on ceremony. Having readied myself to address him using the formal *vous*, out of habit but also for politeness's sake, I now found myself at a loss to know how I should continue. For a moment I stood silent, hesitating between *tu* and *vous*. But the mathematician was unlike anyone I had ever met, so thoroughly himself, it seemed to me, and candid. *Tu* it was, then.

I didn't feel much surprise that he should speak to me so directly; I took it to be in his nature, which struck me as child-like. Indeed it wasn't at all hard to see the erstwhile child in him, as it could be in other men. It was too easy, if anything. His earnest manner of speaking, his socked feet, and gaze – timid yet intent – made you forget all the years that would have brought him to his present height (he stood a fraction under six feet tall) and stature. You could forget that he had a history, and many facets to his personality.

To open our conversation he asked me one or two – routine enough – questions. I barely knew him then, but my impression was that he asked these less for the answers – equally routine – than in order to ask better questions. The best question, I felt, to his way of thinking, would be one that spawned no narrowing answer but instead a dozen expanding follow-up questions simultaneously. And as it happened, this was the kind of conversation I too liked to practise: protean, prone to digressions, free-associative. Soon, we were on to prime numbers and poems, going down lines of mutual enquiry: here was a man after my own mind.

We could have talked then for hours, like old friends reunited after a long separation, but minutes into our conversation one of the organisers came through the door, 'Excusez-moi, Monsieur Tammet, Monsieur Villani, the conference is about to start.'

He showed no sign of stage fright. He lived for mathematics, and talking about mathematics, and the long succession of public events that kept him on the road never appeared to take it out of him; after every conference, another would be allocated a slot in the following month's, or year's, diary. On the contrary, it seemed, all this talking shop replenished his reserves of energy; he craved and thrived on it. One day he'd be down south in Lyon to meet a lab of aspiring physicists, the next, up on stage here in Paris to address a full house of amateurs. He liked mixing things up, addressing everyone, building bridges between the arts and sciences, two worlds which tended otherwise to keep entirely to themselves.

He went to his rucksack then and carefully brought out a pouch and opening it revealed a nest of spider brooches (I counted six), some decorated with red glass, others green, sizes itsy-bitsy to tarantula. He chose one whose sparkly long legs would catch the stage light best and pinned it to his lapel. And then suddenly he remembered his shoes and crouched on the floor putting them on before we headed for the hall.

His talk was about ideas, where they come from, how fragile they are. The topic was well received and would have gone down even better had he not argued for their free circulation, in a spirit of collaboration and not competition, and had he not then shown a lawyer's letter aimed at researchers who published their work not only through the proper channels (that is, steep fee-charging academic journals), but also on a free-to-access digital platform. At which point, coming towards the end of his talk, he almost lost the audience, made up largely of start-up men, entrepreneurs, various manager types, for whom ideas were only as good as the money they earned – the more money, the better the idea.

But as he closed his talk, the audience remembered what they had enjoyed about it and broke into prolonged applause. They indulged his naivety – ordinary 'nutty professor' naivety. They only had to look at the long hair and the wacky clothes. A head in the clouds while others on the ground were busy meeting demand, raising capital, inventing tomorrow. But despite all that – and there was really no two ways about it – what a head! It commanded their respect, their magnanimity. They were softened by his high achieving, his being somebody;

what did it matter if he didn't always talk sense? Besides, he'd gone to the same *grande école*, the same highly selective university in Paris, as many of them; deep down, so they surmised, he was one of them.

Later, over food with friends, I narrated my tête-à-tête with the mathematician and his talk on free ideas before the businessmen. They smiled in all the right places, laughed at the rich men's expense. What a character, your mathematician, they all said.

I couldn't have agreed more. Over the years, seeing each other now and then, he and I stayed in touch.

Why the surprise, Cédric had wondered in 2017, at the news of his entry into national politics? Economists already sat on the benches of the Assembly alongside jurists, teachers and farmers. Surely there was space as well for a mathematician? As in fact there had been in the past – the remote past, admittedly: Gaspard Monge, father of optimal transport theory (one of Cédric's fields of research), had served as minister of the marine under the banner of the Revolution.

Cédric was director of the capital's mathematics research institute at the time the announcement was made. In this capacity he employed a staff of twenty, organised international symposiums and conferences (when he wasn't speaking at them), sought out funding. He was also a scientific advisor to the EU. In short, he liked making things run. It satisfied his passion for order and harmony, for taming an unruly world.

Back in the nineties, at university, he'd even managed to get himself elected student union president. Having so many clubs, events, councils to organise, schedule and chair, made him feel focused and almost calm.

That period was the beginning of his extraordinary social, and sartorial, transformation. How timid – near paralysed by timidity – he had been back then, how heavy his heart when, leaving his family and Toulon at seventeen to board in the capital, he had gone out into the world. The other freshers, he remembered, seemed to him confident, sophisticated, self-aware. They were not above teasing the odd provincial boy so out of place here. 'Call that being dressed, do you?' they guffawed. He glanced down at himself through their eyes and saw the torn blue anorak and shapeless corduroy slacks and beat-up trainers he always wore. He had to do something about them, he suddenly thought – he had to change.

It was not long before he spotted an advertisement in the Métro for historical costumes, with a picture of a ruffle shirt that he thought would lend anyone personality. A few stops from his digs were the city's flea markets, where he could wander, trying on capes and frock coats and top hats. He recalled then pianists he'd seen on stage (piano playing was a family pastime; one of his brothers would become a composer), how chic they looked. Unflappable. He thought of a young James Clerk Maxwell, nineteenth-century author of immense equations – photographed in a romantic three-piece suit. And so, gradually, merging these and other influences, he decided to dress according to his own secret code; to wear nineteenth-century ruffle shirts and a suit and floppy bow ties, to experiment with style and to embrace his quirks and oddness, instead of trying to fit into fashions which made no sense to him, the way they ceaselessly came and went. It was also during this time that he resolved to grow his hair out, to leave it long as it had been when he was a small boy, before it received the chop for school.

His new style found admirers at the university. They touched an ironic finger to his floppy bow tie, saying, 'Looking sharp, man!' and watched his cheeks blush. There was evident pleasure in his face. He was enormously pleased with his new appearance, how it distracted attention from his gawkiness, his limited social skills and lack of small talk. He would take being a hoot any day over being some sad geek. Wherever he went, people came up to compliment him on the get-up. 'You look like a musketeer,' they would say, or 'Chopin's second cousin,' and forgetting his nerves he smiled and told them exactly when and where he'd bought each item.

Classmates became his friends – that, too, was thrillingly new. These friends resolved to round him out. 'You don't know anything,' they told their unworldly companion. There was more to life than chess and piano playing and ping-pong (the only sport he'd ever excelled in). They introduced him to pop and rock music, accompanied him to the cinema where he viewed everything from Bergman to Almodóvar. In return, when they were strolling around an arrondissement, or drinking tea in their digs, he told them all about his studies, about Alan Turing's work on probabilities and James Clerk Maxwell, who, along with Ludwig Boltzmann, gave us statistical mechanics. He told them what he was reading (he was always reading). He couldn't speak more highly of Maxwell's *Treatise on Electricity and Magnetism* and its diagrams which illustrated the invisible lines of force emanating from charged particles. The circular, repeating lines formed beautiful spiderwebs.

The spider brooches, like the pocket watch, would be later

additions to his style. By the time they appeared on his lapel in his thirties, he was an increasingly distinguished professor in Lyon. One day, while browsing the shelves of a local gift and decoration shop, a few minutes' walk from his apartment, he chanced upon the first specimen he ever bought. Encrusted with red glass beads bright in the sun, even dazzling. The thought of wearing it excavated a special pride in him that he could trace all the way back to boyhood. And since he had never done anything by halves, very soon he was collecting spider brooches wherever he travelled.

The presidential contest in 2017 bore no resemblance to any in the history of France's Fifth Republic. The Left and the Right both imploded during the spring campaign – one mired in discord, the other in scandal. All of which left the dark horse centrist candidate, 39-year-old former finance minister Emmanuel Macron, to surge to victory on the promise of a new politics.

Cédric had cast his vote for the new president and he was pleased when the incoming administration pledged to form a government broad enough to include civil society talents. Candidates from every walk of life, it was announced, would be fielded in the legislative races that were to be held in six weeks' time. At once Cédric was approached by members of the presidential party urging him to run. They had just the constituency for him, in the Essonne. As he heard them out, his first instinct was to decline, but he was prevented by their polite insistence. He grew hesitant. He asked around. His wife – a biologist he'd met at university – and their two teenagers, a son and daughter, said they would support him whatever decision he reached. Friends were more divided. He tried to convince them, convince himself: he was forty-three, an age when such opportunities did not always come knocking twice. And here was a chance, perhaps, quite possibly, certainly, to use his time and fame for the greater good.

'Leave mathematics?' asked his colleagues in disbelief. 'You're a pure mathematician and you want to go into politics?' Several tried to alert him to their misgivings. 'You'll be a big catch for them but what's in it for you? Nothing but hassle, I reckon. And think of your research!' Politics, they added, was a murky business, little more than glorified horse-trading and cynical calculations. Those and all the handshakes and selfies. Me-me-me. They didn't have to say that they considered it altogether beneath them.

But Cédric was quite unfazed by their discouragement. He knew full well that many of his fellow mathematicians disdained politics almost as much as the world of television. Just as he also knew that some of these same colleagues would give anything to have their name cited prominently in the journal *Acta Mathematica*, or to be fêted at a symposium in their honour. Whereas his thoughts were increasingly elsewhere: the future of Europe, and the environment, and the scientific advances promised by artificial intelligence.

He realised then that his mind was already made up.

And so, following a short campaign in a university town favourable to the presidential party, he was comfortably elected and took his seat in the Assembly.

Cédric's name was in the headlines, both in France and overseas. In the months, then years, that followed – 2018, 2019 – I,
like many, read with mounting interest the story they told of
his burgeoning career in politics – its various twists and turns –
while maintaining a respectful distance. Conscious of the long
hours he put in, the many competing demands on his time, it
would be several more years before I decided to learn more from
the mathematician himself about his political engagement.

I learned that, back in 2013, Cédric had been asked by the
think tank EuropaNova, on whose administrative board he sat,
to attend a one-on-one meeting at the Elysée Palace. A major
international conference at the Sorbonne was in the works,
heads of several European governments were expected, and the
think tank was counting on a number of France's ministers to
put in an appearance. It was in order to ensure their presence,
and to sort other such matters, that Cédric found himself in the
office of the deputy chief of staff.

The cordial atmosphere was helped by their closeness in
age – the deputy chief of staff was even a little younger than
Cédric. He nodded frequently as Cédric spoke. It would be
sorted, the man said in turn. The ministers would be found.
No problem at all. A strong and united Europe was vital to the
nation's interests. 'Absolutely,' Cédric chimed in. And meeting
his interlocutor's blue eyes – bluer for the crisp white shirt and
rolled-up sleeves – he proceeded to divulge a knowledge on the
topic of the European Union that could have seemed inexhaust-
ible. Furrows of surprise creased the younger man's forehead
as he listened. He had expected the cravat, the spider brooch,
but not this. Had he thought to ask the mathematician where
all this knowledge, this passion, regarding Europe came from,
Cédric would have answered: his family. Italian and Corsican

and Greek blood mingled inside him. His mother's sister lived between Vienna and Brussels, where her Austrian husband was director general of the European Union Military Staff.

Cédric's emotion, it might have been known, had also to do with his father, with losing his father, a mere few weeks before, to a long and painful illness. The son's grief still felt deep and raw. His father was only sixty-three. A man of zany energy, with a rebellious streak, much loved by his students of literature and classics in the south of France, and also a devout scholar of Lucretius, the Latin poet-philosopher for whom everything in the universe emerged from the infinite collisions of swerving atoms.

In another time and place the young deputy chief of staff could have engaged Cédric in a lengthy discussion on teaching Lucretius. He had read philosophy at university and would shortly toy with the idea of dropping politics and launching his own e-learning company.

Before he showed Cédric out he asked for his phone number; and the following summer he texted him to say that his edtech project was starting to look serious. He would need to start thinking about the curricula and hoped that the mathematician might make himself available to advise. Though, as it turned out, the future had other plans. A little while after his text message to Cédric, he was appointed finance minister. Within two years he would launch, not a start-up but a political party. The man's name was Emmanuel Macron.

At the National Assembly the mathematician's arrival roused a dim animus in certain deputies. The Assembly was no place for someone like him, they fumed – Professor Calculus, the new administration's useful idiot. His place was particles and nth dimensions, the invisible and incomprehensible. He should have stayed in his lane, they muttered, in his bubble.

One of the deputies who thought so was the leader of the far-Left party Les Insoumises, Jean-Luc Mélenchon. Ah, the maths wizard, Mélenchon thought, now there's someone who needs setting straight. Would not have the faintest what is inside an employment contract, he thought. Probably imagines workers' rights sprang up overnight. He said as much to the media.

Cédric was not offended. A silly misunderstanding, or else some clumsy joshing of the novice; the old politician had meant no harm. When Cédric bumped into him in the Assembly's corridors he smiled and there followed a friendly exchange of words. Another deputy snapped the moment with his phone and shared the photo on social media. And later that day, at the close of the parliamentary session, Mélenchon walked across the chamber in full view and shook Cédric's hand.

The mathematician-deputy was soon everywhere: on magazine covers and TV, and by the president's side on state visits to Africa, China and the United States. But he also took his parliamentary work seriously. The other deputies could not help but notice. He raised himself in their esteem by his diligent sitting on several commissions, by his thoughtful proposals of new laws (notably on transparency in public life, and animal welfare), by producing a lengthy and detailed national strategy report on artificial intelligence.

Two hundred and thirty-five pages. Longer even than the dense and elaborate mathematical proof he had written in 2009, which had stretched to a hundred and eighty pages and solved a fifty-year-old open problem. For two years he had laboured to prove that the solution of a nonlinear, spatially periodic, close-to-stable-equilibrium Vlasov equation spontaneously evolves towards another equilibrium. Throughout this long labour he had been ably assisted by a younger colleague, Clément Mouhot, with whom he had gone at the problem from various angles, changing tack every time that they got stuck. Until, in a flash of insight, the missing idea had come to him as though out of nowhere, a spark swerving in a corner of his mind and giving birth to an entire new theorem.

Inevitably Cédric's fellow deputies lauded his strategy report far more than they read it. They took in the salient points. Accelerate the development of European AI infrastructures. Train more digital specialists in France. Anticipate the impact of artificial intelligence on the workplace. It was the rare Assembly member who could drill down into the detail – neural networks and algorithms and supercomputers – the parts of the report Cédric had enjoyed writing the most.

Mathematics was never far from his mind and sometimes he missed its simple pleasures. For all the importance of writing a parliamentary report, it had nothing on composing a mathematical proof, which was much like composing a poem, Cédric always thought – the same taut phrasing, the same intuitive yet surprising logic behind the unfolding ideas. The same irresistible quest for truth and beauty. Never would he tire of typing the opening incantation *let* (so and so) *be* (such and such), or the lovely shapeliness imparted by the *if and only if*s. A hundred revisions might separate an initial draft from its final form, a hundred drafts screwed up tight into repellent balls before arriving at the one that would be publishable. He never minded. Each result was its own reward. The main lines of an especially stylish proof could linger in his mind as effortlessly as music.

And music, whether rock or a Prokofiev sonata, had been a constant presence whenever he'd paced back and forth in his study, sitting only to jot equations in a notebook or revise a step in his reasoning. He liked listening to a French folk ballad he'd heard his parents play when he was a boy. A song about passion and letting go: 'I want to be capable of loving you, for two years, three years, ten,' the balladeer sings, 'loving you till the strength to love you fails me . . . so that I might love someone else.' Cédric knew all the words, every note and intake of breath; he'd played the song that many times.

Even on those evenings and weekends when he'd been on his own, his wife and children staying with grandparents, he would close the door of his study behind him as he worked, as if not wanting to let the music out. Pacing always in his deep-thinking clothes – some loose T-shirt in summer, in winter a baggy sweater. Up all hours. Endless evenings during those two years working on the theorem, spent with his music (on low when the children were home and sleeping) and laptop and pen and paper, unable to leave this or that formula alone, carried further and further away by his thoughts – perhaps only an earthquake might have shaken him out of them.

'Marsu,' his wife might have wished to whisper from the doorway, using the nickname given to him at uni for his bouncy way of pacing around. 'Do you know what time it is? Hello, hello? Earth to Marsu.'

But she knew well enough when to leave him with his equations.

They were everywhere in his parliamentary work too, Cédric thought, though perhaps he alone in the Assembly saw them in the pie and bar charts displayed in committee presentations, or in the statistics cited during a debate in the lower chamber.

He alone might glimpse an intriguing possible link between, say, the nation's income distribution and the Boltzmann distribution in statistical physics. Some part of him then could feel lonely, having such singular thoughts in the midst of these rowdy politicians who frequently shouted over one another until called to order by the speaker. But another part of him, much the larger, was thoroughly used to thinking apart and at ease doing so. He always had.

Sometimes, coming out of the Assembly into the soothing dark of a late spring evening, Cédric thought he would like nothing better in that instant than to take to the city's streets as in his student days, to walk his thoughts, or else simply to observe the surrounding facades and faces as he strolled. He loved Paris in these hours when the streets seemed to grow wider and the passers-by were often merry. He relived the stirring nights when he and several university classmates had chased each other through these same cobbled streets into the small hours in a version of the game called hare and hounds; the 'hounds' pursuing not a trail of chalk or paper but calls made at successive phone booths, each booth approaching the city centre and the students' dorms.

He remembered those nights with a double nostalgia, when on the trail of a classmate, getting high on the chase and lured by the approaching solution, he'd experienced the same rush he'd felt as an introverted child engrossed in his favourite detective tales, French translations of *The Three Investigators*. He'd come a long, long way indeed.

Several of these streets were named after mathematicians:

Rue Laplace, Rue Sophie-Germain. It occurred to him that perhaps someday in the future his own name would likewise be given to a street here. There was already a theory of curvature named after him – the Lott-Sturm-Villani theory – a recognition of his ever-growing legacy.

In September 2019, putting an end to a summer of speculation, Cédric made it known that he was running for mayor of Paris. His candidacy was likely doomed from the outset, since he was obliged to go up against his own party.

All summer the government had tried and failed to talk him out of running as an independent. The official candidate – a rather bland apparatchik in a suit, a safe pair of hands – had been selected internally in early July, through the proper channels, a spokesman insisted. It was suggested by some that this decision had come from the top – President Macron had long ago made up his mind. In any event, now was the time to pull together as a party and as a movement, they all said. You owe us your loyalty, they told Cédric, don't you?

But no, the mathematician did not seem to think in such terms. He hadn't acquired the politicians' social codes, or else having done so seemed willing to transgress them when he believed they were unfair.

Cédric had sought the party's backing for his mayoral run in the beginning, only to finish well and truly stitched up. The party had chosen to disregard all the polls that showed him to be by far the most popular contender with the voters. They had ignored the numerous artists, scientists and public intellectuals who had come out in favour of Cédric's candidacy. They had gone back on the promise of a new politics which he (and they themselves) had been elected to embody. How then, in all good conscience, could he simply swallow his words and fall in line behind the other man?

The guy's an idiot, the apparatchik's team concluded bitterly after months of futile back-and-forth. He's going to split our vote and gift Paris – a city of two million – to our opponents. No one could say they hadn't tried to reason with him. To help him digest his disappointment they had made all the right noises about involving him in a manifesto that would be as bold as it would be inclusive. They had alternated between the carrot – Cédric Villani, Minister of Higher Education and Research, how did that sound? – and then the stick: he would risk exclusion from the party if he persevered. When nothing else worked they had asked him to think of his health and his family. Was he really tough enough for such a long and bruising campaign?

He would not be cowed, though. 'Tough' was not his conception of a good politician. He knew – for the comments had been leaked to the press – what the party's candidate thought of him: 'He won't see the blows coming, he'll get taken apart.' To this provocation, dignified silence had been his sole response. Careless of the threats and warnings, he had continued conferring with potential allies all through the summer months. His eventual campaign launch, from a café-bistro in the fourteenth arrondissement, had attracted photographers and reporters and a scrum of cameramen.

A lyrical, impassioned Cédric addressed the packed room. 'Building teams to solve complex problems has been my life's work,' he noted, 'even before I entered politics.' He promised to put technology, science and knowledge at the heart of his campaign. He would fight for a Paris unbeholden to financial speculators; a greener Paris in which it was possible to breathe. A Paris in which distance from the city centre no longer enclaved entire districts.

He would always put Paris before his party, he said.

After ten minutes came the moment everyone who had managed to squeeze inside the café had been waiting for. Cédric's overexcited voice almost ran away from him as he cried out, 'I announce to you on this fourth of September that I have decided to run for mayor.' At these closing words his face, so animated only seconds before, went blank with bewilderment. He gazed in astonishment at the joyous tumult he had just unleashed.

'Vill-a-ni!' chanted the crowd. 'Pa-ris! Vill-a-ni! Pa-ris!'

It was not long past seven o'clock in the evening and every news channel in the country carried the launch live. The candidate's voice and delivery and the confused look of wonder on his face went instantly viral.

As he stepped aside from the podium, the crowd swirled around him in a confused melee, tugging his sleeves and almost spilling him out into the street. He had made it outside when his spider brooch was swept from his lapel and had to be recovered from beneath the trampling shoes.

The brooches Cédric wore now on the campaign trail were smaller than some of his other spiders, and had less pizzazz than those decorated with brightly coloured beads. On the advice of his team, he also tucked his cravat, often a folded blue one, neatly inside his suit; while some days the cravat vanished altogether, to leave his collar open. In a further concession to respectability, his long hair and old-world beard, the latter cultivated since he had become a deputy, both received a trim. The result of these adjustments was a greater focus (or so it was hoped) on what the candidate said, at the expense of a style which had long made his reputation for eccentricity. It was hoped that when Paris's voters saw him on TV or in the flesh they would see a plausible future mayor instead of 'Cédric the Eccentric' or 'Spider Man' as he had occasionally been dubbed.

But for these – rather modest – adjustments to his clothes and hair Cédric did not change. He never had any bad words for anyone. Not even for the party's designated candidate, who could be snide and abrasive and with whom no reconciliation proved possible. 'My door is always open,' the apparatchik said coldly when reporters broached Cédric's independent run. 'I offer him the hand of friendship.'

The pudgy man's hands were one reason why Cédric felt no animosity towards him. The fingernails, Cédric had noticed when the men met behind closed doors to air their differences, though clean and pink were thoroughly chewed.

Cédric recognised the nervous habit from his own boyhood, except that the object of Cédric's chewing had been a sweater he wore in primary school. His sweater had been the record of his mute perplexity during lessons: hole after hole in the wool where he'd gathered up the collar between his teeth and nibbled anxiously. The confusing shifts between subjects, the pressure to keep up and still, the unspoken rules that no teacher cared to explain and that could land you in the naughty corner – all these served to deepen his already shy and solitary nature. As the other children spoke and sang in class, the wool's ticklish taste in his mouth had been strangely comforting. He'd let countless right answers go unpronounced that way, his arm too rigid with nerves to raise it, the distance between his brain and tongue seeming infinitely long.

Cédric's private talks with his rival were as short as each man's team had expected. Far longer, if no more satisfying, were some of the brainstorming sessions at his campaign HQ. It was a feature of politics he didn't relish, the exhaustive discussions of tactics with his advisors; everyone's energies, he could not help thinking, would be so much better spent developing policy instead of trying to get one over on the other parties. Moreover, these conclaves had an unpleasant tendency to drag.

Back when Cédric had directed the capital's mathematics research institute there had been plenty such powwows in his office. But he had never permitted them to overrun. A small sandglass flipped at each turn encouraged the participants to cut to the chase. From time to time, whenever he listened with one ear, he found his mind drawn to the constant motion of the whispery sand, the grains' obedient journeys, so unlike the freewheeling molecules in a gas.

The polls were rather promising. They showed Cédric and the party's nominee in a statistical tie – each on 15–17 per cent – within a few points of the sitting mayor, Anne Hidalgo, who was on 24 per cent. Crunching these numbers, Cédric's team felt confident that the mayor's lead over him could be closed.

'Voters like you,' they told Cédric. 'They like you very much. But we have to bear in mind that popularity doesn't always translate into votes. So we have to get you out there, show that you understand people's everyday issues. Campaign stops in schools and shops and hospitals are all well and good, but we also need you hitting the pavement.'

Cédric nodded in assent. An open-air market was chosen

to take him to one morning the following week. Those who flanked him, ready to hand out campaign leaflets, felt on edge; in such a setting anything could happen. What if their candidate made a fool of himself? It was one thing knowing how to give a good speech or lecture, quite another to talk to the average voter in the street.

Some of the buyers in the market pulled back when they saw Cédric approach, not wanting to feel dull in the face of his brilliance. They were men and women who had left school without academic qualifications, unable to make head or tail of algebra and geometry and all the rest of that airy-fairy business, and the feeling of shame or inferiority clung to them even after all these years.

But when they heard their aspiring mayor respond warmly to a fishmonger's *bonjour*, all nerves went from them. He did not sound or look one bit like a politician, he had that much going for him. And he didn't sound like a mathematician either, they thought, not that they knew what a mathematician sounded like.

'How old is he?' an onlooker asked her friend. 'He has such a young face.'

The other woman googled him on her phone. 'Forty-six.'

'No! Where do you get that from?'

'Wikipedia.'

'Ah, well, if Wikipedia says so,' snorted the woman.

But it was true. And the woman was quite right – the candidate did not look his age.

Other phones climbed out of pockets, filmed the scene, inched closer. And alongside them, shoppers with their baskets and grocery bags, curious tourists, the murmur of a small crowd.

Cédric

Cédric posed for picture takers, let them snap away. They photographed his good side, his bad side. They photographed him reaching over a fruit stall; meeting a vigorous handshake; listening to someone's overlong question. They photographed the suit and the spider and the concentration that was written in capital letters on his face.

The long question concerned housing. 'Rent's crazy here,' the middle-aged man complained. Cédric nodded; he did not interrupt. And when at last the questioner relented, he replied thoughtfully. He insulted nobody's intelligence. He did not pretend to have all the answers. He addressed the have-nots just as he did the haves.

People at other markets, on other mornings, brought all sorts of questions to him, on low salaries and dirty pavements, street muggings and trains that never arrived on time, and not one did he duck. His gaze, as he spoke, could be disconcerting – so intense and direct.

He was being himself, transparent and candid to a fault. And that was perhaps the problem. Many voters, though they told themselves otherwise, did not expect candour in their candidates. They did not want to hear things told straight. They wanted things told slant, the better to conform to their desires and preconceptions. A good politician should be all things to everyone – that was the gist of what they thought.

Could the buyers and sellers at these markets see themselves voting for him? He wasn't cut out for politics, some said, he should have stuck to the maths; others affirmed that he had been courageous to pursue his candidacy. They debated whether or not he was telling truth to power, and, if so, which truth precisely was he telling it?

He might look funny and express himself funnily, thought a

187

woman buying cheese, but at least he listens. He's not like the rest of them.

"Course he'll never win,' a father said to his son. 'Shame really. CV longer than my arm, prizes galore plus a *Légion d'honneur*. Cleverer than the other candidates put together.'

The party pulled its punches with him, at least to begin with. How little they knew him to imagine that he would eventually tire and drop out. The dawning realisation that he wouldn't, hit them hard. They began intriguing against him.

Towards the end of November, as he remained steady in the polls, Cédric was made aware of certain remarks about him that were circulating. Not only was he proper weird, it was being whispered, and completely out of his depth, he was borderline Asperger's. He was *autistic*.

Paris's voters deserved to know, was the implication. The mathematician's backers were guilty of manipulating him; they were irresponsible. Poor thing, the gossipers sighed in mock concern. Crashing to defeat would be sure to bring on a nervous breakdown.

However, the butt of these rumours and innuendo did not anger. It was his nature to recoil from gossip, for which he had neither time nor patience. Finally, though, displeased that it might be said that he was concealing something, Cédric determined that he would respond to the rumours publicly. He would not deny who he was; he would lose the election, lose it by a landslide, sooner than do so.

'Am I autistic? Perhaps I am,' he told a journalist for *Vanity Fair*, and then, a few days later, an interviewer on national TV.

He couldn't say for sure because he had never been formally diagnosed.

And, anyway, he added, 'What difference would it make?'

From his earliest years, in the middle of the French country-side, his had been an insulated childhood, he recalled. The shouty red of poppies, an old bicycle rusting in the grass, busy dust motes lit by the sun and making his chest hurt: these were the delicate child's first impressions of the world. He had had trouble breathing, whether from nerves and senses that worked overtime, or from bouts of asthma and bronchitis which laid him up for weeks on end, and his parents put an ear to his chest and gave him aspirin dissolved in a glass of fizzing water. *Psssst*, the glass seemed to say as he lifted it to his lips, *psssst*, as though it had some pressing secret to share.

He was reading on his own by the age of four, paging through books his parents had brought to his room and helped him to decipher. The paediatrician who saw him that summer was amazed. On the doctor's desk was a newspaper and he showed its front page to the little boy. Cédric read aloud, 'The mortal remains of Paul V I . . .'

'Paul the Sixth,' corrected the doctor.

'. . . will be transferred Wednesday afternoon from C—, Cas—'

'Castel Gandolfo.'

'. . . near Rome,' continued Cédric, 'to St Peter's Basilica.'

'Bravo,' the paediatrician said to the boy; 'remarkable,' he said to the parents, who were both, he learned, teachers of lit-erature. They explained how their son spent hours every day reading and rereading his books. His favourites were long on science, books about dinosaurs and the universe. He could tell an ankylosaurus from a protoceratops, recite all the planets in the solar system, yet he did not know the word for a poodle (*caniche*) or the names of the seasons. (And neither of these would he learn for several more years.)

One day his father brought home from the flea market a Disney comic book, *Donald in Mathmagic Land*. Suddenly, little Cédric couldn't read enough of square tree roots and imaginary triangles and birds who sang the opening digits of pi. He took a great interest in chess; it was Grandmother, he remembered, who taught him how to play. His grandmother was an elegant woman who knew her own intelligence; had she been born a man, or fifty years later, she would have become a historian. She was a direct descendant of Demetrio Stefanopoli, count of Comnène, and, through this count, of the Byzantine royal house of Komnenos.

Chess, chess and more chess. For several months this became more or less Cédric's life, playing the royal game to the point of obsession, before his father intervened. His father confiscated his board and pieces, not wanting the six-year-old to turn into a mad prodigy. He had followed media reports of what the game had done to Bobby Fischer. He didn't want his son to grow into a future like that. This was not long before the family moved to Toulon and Cédric began primary school.

Cédric must have cried at the loss of his chess set. But as the obsession faded it was replaced by another, fortified by the maths puzzles he tackled in class, and which would prove far more lasting. Mathematics, he was discovering, was delightfully unambiguous, its rules self-explanatory; that is, the moment you grasped their logic. Playing with these rules, code-breaking, puzzle-solving, he could happily neglect the regular problems of having no friends, of being teased or shirked for being so very different to the other children.

For all these problems, he never hated tomorrow. Tomorrow, whether he was spending it in class or inside his books, always had something new to teach him.

Soon he'd become hooked too on mystery stories, another form of puzzle, honing his powers of deduction with the likes of Sherlock Holmes and Arsène Lupin, unmasking the tales' baddies the same way, in class, he figured out the true identities of an equation's Y and Z. He devoured the escapades of *The Three Investigators*, whose heroes were close to his age, almost overcome by a desire to join them, since with them, at least, he felt he would belong.

In December 2019, at the Trianon theatre, Cédric gave a speech on stage before hundreds of his supporters.

'I've read and heard so many things, seen so many attacks, sometimes concerning my policies, often concerning my person. I've said it before: being different is a strength.'

He paused for the clapping, looked out at the rows of upturned faces.

'They'll tell you that I am mad or that my project cannot succeed. My friends, the true madness would be to hope for change yet vote for the same old parties.'

His campaign for mayor, he knew, had stalled; the polls placed him on low double digits. At least the interviews he had given on his possible autism had been universally well received. Politicians on all sides had saluted his courage, the dignity in his response, including the ones who had themselves spurred on the rumours. If Cédric smiled at their hypocrisy he did not resent it; he had far better uses for his energy.

Whenever he asked himself why he was running he decided that he hoped to redistribute power. Winning it interested him less than making it flow more freely, more efficiently. His manifesto imagined a citizens' assembly, in which experts and ordinary Parisians drawn by lots would contribute to the mayor's decision-making. Only then, Cédric thought, when power became less concentrated in a few hands, might change be enacted at the level of voters' needs and values.

On posters, in conference halls, via interviews in the media, the candidates' visions, their different Parises, called out to these voters, but increasingly people turned their attention elsewhere. In the New Year, they watched reports from Wuhan about a 'mysterious pneumonia' that would soon dominate the headlines. The election, which was to be held at the start of spring, having for months seemed rather exciting, appeared suddenly pointless, and finally dangerous.

The result was, in the end, a foregone conclusion. Most of the Parisians who bothered, or dared, to cast their vote in March, just before the first lockdown, favoured continuity. The incumbent prevailed easily, ahead of the Right and the presidential party which came in third. Cédric, the outsider, trailed in fifth, on 7 per cent.

When Cédric returned to the Assembly's benches, he sat as an independent. And when, at the end of his term, he sought to retain his seat in the Essonne, the presidential party opposed him. The ensuing contest was tight; the winner unknown until the very last of the thirty-seven thousand ballots had been counted. Cédric conceded after losing by a margin of eighteen votes.

He had just returned from a vacation in the mountains of Colombia when I told Cédric about the narrative portrait of him that I envisaged writing. It was May 2023, almost a year since he had left politics and Paris; he was once more a professor of mathematics in Lyon. We were video-calling late on this particular evening and he was casual in jeans and a zip-up sweatshirt. Although jet-lagged, he looked well. 'I turn fifty in October.'

As he shared memories of his childhood, he told me about *The Three Investigators*, a series of books I had not come across myself. He had read the French editions by the dozen, he said, and I imagined the little Cédric soaking up each story, enthralled and no longer lonely.

In the story Cédric mentioned to me – *The Mystery of the Silver Spider* – the action takes place in a tiny European kingdom named Varania. Here power is enshrined in a crown jewel possessing the form of a spider. The pint-size heroes arrive on an urgent mission: palace plotters have seized the jewel, and plan to turn the country into an international haven for law-dodgers. Gathering all their wits and pluck, the three boys figure out where the jewel has been hidden and so foil the coup.

To reward their ingenuity and daring, the Order of the Silver Spider – the kingdom's highest honour – is pinned on their three proud chests. The Silver Spider, the boys learn, is worn on a chain by the monarch at each coronation. Far more than a jewel, it is a symbol of everything the Varanians cherish: freedom, independence and the common good.

As he had read the story, Cédric, in his mind the fourth investigator, became an honorary Varanian too, vowing to uphold those same values.

Ayo

It was early morning after a day which had begun innocently enough and the house seemed to hold its breath. The sun came into rooms still scarred from the afternoon before. There had been some clearing of the worst by then, some semblance of order restored, and Ayo's mother was in the kitchen making noise with the pots and pans, a deliberate hum of activity asking to be thought ordinary but which could feel like solicitude. Ayo was leaving her bedroom when the pots and pans fell silent, and she heard her mother calling her name. Her mother's voice today was different from the one she used with yesterday's guests to the compound. It was lower now. Raw. And tentative. Ayo approached but did not enter the kitchen. Instead she dithered at the threshold. At least the kitchen still looks and smells as it always has, she thought.

'Ayo, go wake your little sister.' That was what she was expecting to hear any second. In fact, she had already started to half turn when she heard her mother say something else.

'What?' said Ayo, turning back.

'Ayo, come here please,' Toyin repeated softly. Then, when her daughter did not, she walked over and leaned down and held the little hand that had been worrying the hem of a green pyjama top.

'Did you get some sleep? Are you hungry?' She searched her daughter's face as she spoke. 'I wouldn't blame you if you weren't hungry. After yesterday. What happened. But you really should get something down you.'

Ayo did not move. 'I'm okay,' she said, rubbing an elbow with her free hand. 'I wasn't hurt.'

'To God be the glory! You were very strong. You know, your father and I spoke on the phone last night. We had a long conversation. About yesterday. About our future. We made some decisions. And now there's no reason to be afraid, none at all, because it won't ever happen again.'

Ayo, who had been looking down at the floor as her mother spoke, said nothing for a moment. Then she said again, very quietly, 'I wasn't hurt.'

'No. But you could have been. Your father agrees with me. What happened here was the last straw for us. Ayo, look at me. The only thing that matters is your safety, yours and your sisters'.'

She couldn't return her mother's gaze for long. A memory from the afternoon flashed through her mind; she was on her elbows and knees, panting, hiding her little sister under the bed. The sister was too young to understand. 'She's still sleeping,' Ayo said now.

Toyin nodded, released her daughter's hand and straightened up. 'Go wake her, please.'

Ayo Sokale spoke, in 2020s fashion, to the recording camera of her phone. Behind her stood only the beige wall that served as a neutral background. The camera shook as she spoke; no one had thought about a tripod. She was wearing a black turtleneck and an expression of sustained concentration. 'There's no one look for an autistic person,' she was saying. 'We don't all look the same.'

Ayo is a civil and coastal engineer. She is not yet thirty and lives in the Thames Valley, in Berkshire. ICE, the Institution of Civil Engineers, uploaded her one-minute clip, one of several, to its video channel in the spring of 2021. Exactly twenty years after she and her family left Nigeria.

By chance I came across her clip one day, while watching videos on the Internet. I probably shouldn't say 'by chance'. Probably the clip reached my screen on account of my recent viewing history, of some algorithm which – this time at least – had successfully read my thoughts.

'We don't all look the same.' It felt familiar to me, a neurodivergent writer, this modern exercise of 'raising awareness', and the reason it felt familiar was that I had similarly lent myself to it in the past. Speaking to a camera, in 2000s and 2010s fashion, with a TV cameraman manning it. Using a word like 'Asperger's' – as was employed then – to describe a life, a way of seeing and being in the world.

But that was as far as the similarity went. I had no clear idea back then that I might be 'speaking out', or braving the attitudes and expectations of viewers. And, unlike Ayo's generation, I had felt neither the consolation, nor the responsibility, of belonging to a group. It would never have occurred to me to say 'we', only 'I'.

She wasn't hard to find. She had a website. After I had been in touch, after showing my credentials and earning her confidence, we got to talking on a semi-regular basis. The Ayo on our video calls was the same Ayo I'd seen in the clip: articulate, thoughtful and candid. And there was something else beyond these qualities, attractive and essential as they are, that had made me want to write about her. She was *vibrant*.

She would find thirty minutes for me here, three-quarters of an hour there. Even that took quite some doing – pretty much every waking hour of her day being accounted for. She has only to look at the time to be told where she ought to be.

I had no plan as such and few prepared questions. As much as possible, I wanted to keep our conversations open-ended. I thought we might talk about her engineering career, then jump back to her childhood move to England, then who knew? But that's not quite how things turned out. Our exchanges took sharp, surprising detours – disorientating and fascinating in equal measure.

I had thought her brave; I hadn't known the half of it.

Dr Sokale worked for an NHS hospital in England, and when his wife's waters broke, one freezing February day, he welcomed the arrival of their second daughter, Ayo.

Toyin brought the baby home to her native city of Ibadan. Her husband, like many Nigerian doctors who work for the NHS, would visit his wife and children two or three times a year.

The Sokale sisters shared a large house in Bashorun, Water Reservoir Area, with their mother, aunt and older cousins. The house stood inside a compound whose walls were high, its gates surveilled. Bougainvillea brightened these walls, while palms and mango and guava trees flourished within – an intrepid cousin might occasionally fall from the lower branches, like ripe fruit. On Sundays, dressed for church, the three sisters would not climb a limb of any tree; they would be too busy curtsying to the grown-ups who lunched at the house after the service. Or, ahead of that, laying the table, or, helping out in the kitchen, or getting under the maid's feet as they rustled and bustled. There was a rigour in the house, but guests were always a welcome sight. They would be ladies from the church, wearing wrappers and headgear, smiling broadly and smelling the beef stew, pounded yam and okra as they entered.

Ayo liked sitting up with the ladies, saying grace, watching the women eat, the eldest always first to begin, copying their fingers as they moulded the doughy yam into scoops, seeing the beef on the plates linger till the end before disappearing, as good table manners required. The beef was lean and spicy. When it disappeared, the women talked at last. They praised their host (after the Lord), shared recipe tips, complained about the rising prices. 'You go to market with your seventy naira and when you get there they tell you it is now ninety or one hundred.' Some talked about their husbands overseas, and others their children's grades in class, and Toyin passed around the report cards that came to the house in her daughters' satchels, each commending their cleanliness – grade A – and high marks, and stating, for instance, that Ayotunde is a well-behaved and diligent student.

The women had all known Ayo since her babbling days. Such a quiet and intent child. Older than her years. Always taking her toys apart and putting them back together again. Not dolls. Cars and trucks. They would tease her gently: did she remember the time she ran them ragged searching all over for her? Searching for what seemed like hours, they turned the compound upside down until, aah, at last, there she was snoozing behind the curtain in the living room, a toy truck beside her with its engine in pieces, snoozing all the time they'd been rushing and thumping from room to room calling out, 'A-yo!'

She remembered. Or perhaps it was only the ladies' story that she remembered, she had heard it told so many times.

'Yes, Aunty,' Ayo would say each time she heard the tale. 'I was very small but I remember.'

She was glad to be drawn into their discussions. With the ladies she was not reserved. She comported herself like a little lady, a lady eight years old, and had learned what never to do. Speak up before an adult addresses you. Talk back. Draw attention to yourself. She could sit up so straight and still that you might forget that she was there. The women approved. None would ever think to say to her, 'Go along and play with the other children.' There was a feeling, unspoken but understood, that the child's place was with them, more than with girls and boys her age. They thought of her separately, even from her own siblings. 'Ayo and her sisters', they would say.

One Sunday afternoon, the one that would change everything, after the ladies and maid left early, a mother and daughter called by. The little girl attended the same school as Ayo and her younger sister. (The eldest boarded in another city.) On this Sunday the compound found itself emptier than usual, the aunt and her children, and neighbours, all away for the weekend; even the guard ordinarily at the gate had the afternoon off. There were not enough eyes to go around, and so Ayo reluctantly agreed to keep hers on the playmates. She sat on her bed and watched the girls playing on the rug as they dressed and undressed their silly dolls. Now and then peals of laughter blurted out from behind the closed living-room door, and made her heart shrink. She felt a painful distance open up between her and the suddenly strange world of adults.

She could not know that these minutes were the calm before the storm. That soon after, the Sokales would have to bid farewell to the compound, to its bougainvillea and mangoes, trees bearing guavas and intrepid cousins.

It was an hour later in the afternoon that Toyin accompanied her guests out of the compound to their car, and waved them off. A little way down the road, where delivery drivers parked, two young men were waiting in a beat-up Volvo. Toyin didn't give it or its occupants another thought until, on her way back towards the gates, she felt their pistol wedge painfully in her ribs. The armed man told her not to make a sound if she knew what was good for her.

And as they barged her inside the compound and locked the gates their features disappeared beneath bandanas, their hands inside gloves.

'I'm coming,' Toyin had said to her daughters as she went out, and by this she meant 'back in a moment'. The sisters began to tidy their room, since homework beckoned. At a gravelly sound outside the house Ayo turned to the window and saw unfamiliar shadows approaching. Get down, she tried to say. Her little sister stood near her. A tide of fear picked her up then and swept them both under her bed. Not ten seconds later the front door burst open, then they heard a male voice, terse and threatening. They heard a man in the living room yank what sounded like the telephone from the wall. The voice grew louder and terser; the voice and the heavy footsteps that came into their room were those of no 'uncle' Ayo knew. 'Comot,' the voice shouted in Pidgin. 'Comot from under dere or I go come get you bot' self.'

Ayo heard her mother calling her name from the sofa. 'Do what the man says.'

So the sisters did. They were taken to Toyin, across a floor covered with dirt and dust carried in by the burglars. In front of them stood the other man with his bloodshot eyes and his finger on the trigger.

For a moment the men said nothing, as if they were extorting only silence from the house. Then the one without the gun asked Toyin where she kept her money. Where, he asked again and again, always in the same words, when she answered that there was hardly a kobo coin in the house. 'My purse,' she said. Take my purse. It's in my bag.' It held her ATM cards. And there was her jewellery in her bedroom drawer. Also the wedding band she wore.

She sounded odd when she said this as if her tongue had doubled in size, so that it stumbled over even the most ordinary words: 'please' and 'take' and 'leave'.

'Is dat all?' Now it was the gunman's turn to shout. 'Na lie! Abeg no try me, I dey tell you.' He levelled the gun at Ayo's temple as he said this.

And yet Ayo at gunpoint remained calm, extraordinarily calm. It didn't enter her head to budge. Sitting so deadly still and silent hardly went against her nature; on the contrary, gripped as she often was by some lengthy daydream, or Bollywood film on TV, she would do just that – sit and stare ahead into the near or far distance, sometimes for hours.

Though this was different; what she was seeing here was not one bit of her choosing. Nor to her liking. She did not know these men, knew only that they were 'bad men' and wished so

hard that they would leave. Leave with the purse and the jewellery, her sister's dolls and her toy trucks, leave with the roof
and rooms and all the trees too if they could carry them off but
leave. And yet still she could not bring herself to see the most
frightening side of the situation. The bullet (assuming there
was one) waiting inches from her temple. But how could she
see, or feel, a thing when she was no longer there? When she
was, as she was in that moment, entering some new knowledge
of herself. Some secret but necessary steeliness; also a lightness, lifting her far, far away. A dimension of resilience.

'Dem get plenty plenty paper.'

It was the gunman's accomplice yelling from the adults'
bedrooms. He had laid his gloved hand on the family's green
passports. Let loose sheaves of letters from a distant husband,
stamped the children's birth certificates with his grimy boot,
scattered photos – the girls with their grandmother; Ayo in her
first school uniform; Toyin and the doctor's big day.

The passports were enough to pacify the thieves, who could
sell them on for a good price. As the late afternoon faded into
evening, they turned on their heels with their modest haul and
fled, leaving behind the pulled-out drawers, rifled-through
clothes, smashed toys and other debris.

Toyin released the latest breath she had been holding in.

Once their warm cups of Bournvita had been drained, and
pyjamas squirmed into, the sisters were tucked in – by the light
of a bedside lamp that stayed on – and closed their eyes tight
and did not sleep. Until, at long last, they did.

Weeks later the Sokales collected their newly issued passports
and boarded a plane bound for England.

At any one time, Ayo will have a dozen or more tabs open on her phone. A dozen is on the low side for her; many days, it's more like scores. Scores and scores, as many as her phone can manage. One takes you to a page about Fallingwater House. Another to the website of Welwyn Garden City. A third to a long list of motivational quotes. But often and before very long she will leave all these for other pages around a common theme. A name.

She has only to begin googling tomorrow's weather or a T-shirt in her size or to graze the T-key with the tip of her finger, and the search box guesses 'Tesla'. The name relegates every alternative her phone auto-suggests. That goes for 'TV' and 'takeaway' and 'tax return' and other common results that start with English's twentieth letter. The search engine's algorithm likely takes her for some nervy shareholder with stock in Tesla Inc., or an electric car obsessive hunting for the latest model, but the truth is she doesn't hold any shares or care particularly about this or that brand of car. Each time she types the name into an online search she means the person who made it famous. 'Tesla' as in Nikola Tesla, inventor and – like herself – engineer.

She must have looked up his story a zillion times already. A zillion times gone to the Internet to read about his inspirational life and work. Her phone knows the details by now, forwards and backwards and inside out. His dates, 1856–1943, and his birthplace, the rural village Smiljan – so easy to misspell – in what is today Croatia. His unusual mind, vast learning and vaster imagination, which speak so powerfully to her. Hundreds of patents, inventions galore. The X-ray, radio, neon tubes, even the smartphone she is holding.

On a web page of a science institute she has come across a fabulous photo of him in his laboratory. The photo is in black and white, but she can't help seeing it in colour – the branching violet sparks from gigantic coils flashing above his pomaded head. Like the bolt of lightning that flared over his family's roof just as he was born.

As a boy, Tesla developed a prodigious gift for envisioning contraptions that did not yet exist. Ayo has read that he would envisage every nut and bolt, put them together in his head and leave the device running in some corner of his mind, only to return to it weeks or months afterwards to check for any wear and tear.

She taps other tabs, gets up other pages on her screen. She reads how Tesla swapped Austro-Hungary for America, sailing to New York at her age, twenty-eight, with barely a dime to his name, in one pocket his passenger ticket alongside a pair of gloves – their fingers crossed, at least that is how Ayo imagines them – the other pocket containing a letter of recommendation dated May 1884 and addressed to one Thomas Edison.

'The Wizard of Menlo Park' hired him, but Tesla would not see a cent of the $50,000 of funding Edison had promised. When he tried going it alone, men in suits made further profits on Tesla's naivety; they stole his patents, reducing him to digging ditches in wintertime for two lousy dollars a day.

It was Edison's rival, Westinghouse, who allowed Tesla to shine. With his backing, Tesla helped to build the world's first large-scale hydroelectric plant at Niagara Falls – it delights Ayo no end that his turbines ran on fast cascading water. How green and renewable and ahead of his time! She has always marvelled at the lengths, the heights, the depths that water can go to. She thrills at the Falls' size and flow urging Tesla's turbine motors to turn, and turning water into watts – the energy so harnessed electrifying whole cities.

Of course, that snake Edison was fuming. He cursed the competition. A popular science magazine article that Ayo clicks on describes his cunning scheme to discredit Tesla. Reporters were summoned to take down Edison's words. Gentlemen of the press, my rival uses alternating current, not direct current as I do. See what happens when I pull this switch: and he sends thousands of A/C volts through a dog, a calf, a horse (even, years later, an elephant). As if electrocuting animals weren't shocking enough, he set his sights on a prisoner, and financed the making of what became the electric chair.

Edison's mud, though, wouldn't stick. Tesla's reputation survived. He had no appetite for fame and fortune, in any case, and let both dwindle, shying away from people and prizes as he got older. In his later years he dreamed of free energy for all, and technology that would make war impracticable. Ayo is moved by the audacity.

She has turned off her phone and is in her kitchen seeing what there is for dinner. As she puts the water on for the rice something comes to her, an anecdote remembered from her scattered reading about the inventor. Whenever he sat down to eat, he would always work out how many grams there were on his plate. She takes her phone's word for it. She does something a little similar herself, come to think of it, with the rice and so on. But she doesn't eat alone as he would do. Alone, she assumes, because he was so sensitive to certain sounds that pass most people by unnoticed – their chewing and swallowing and slurping. And not only sounds, certain shapes and textures too: he was repelled by pearls; the very sight of them curled his toes – even the most beautiful woman in the world he would send packing if she happened to be wearing pearls. For that matter he abhorred all the jewellery that men and women wore, the chains and bracelets and the jittery earrings and the rings clinging on various fingers. He ate his dinner late for Americans (but perhaps not for Austro-Hungarians) – Ayo remembers the exact time: 8.10 p.m., always ten minutes past eight in the evening because 810 can be divided by 3, and then again by 3 cubed ($3 \times 3 \times 3$). Ayo is the kind of person for whom this makes beautiful sense.

It is hard to explain but she feels protective towards him, absurdly so she knows, for what could her protectiveness mean to a man eighty years dead and, for most of them, forgotten? Not so forgotten these days. Not now that the devices running in his head for decades are being rediscovered – ideas that, in some, court wonder; in others, bafflement.

A loner, she has read some call him, an oddball, an eccentric.

Eccentric he might have been, she thinks, but at least he is our eccentric. When Ayo says 'we' – the 'we' of her neurodiversity clip – she includes Nikola Tesla.

Why did you leave Africa, Ayo would be asked when, months after the burglary at the compound, she found herself in a playground in Eastbourne, a pebble's throw from the eroding edge of southern England.

She knew better than to say anything about guns.

What kind of a name is Ayo anyway, the children enquired as they flocked out of the gates after class. And her hair, talk about frizzy! Girls snorted at the jumpers she wore even in sticky June. Always following us around, like she don't get it. So blank and stiff.

They had her all wrong. They never heard her singing along to her mother's radio in the kitchen of her new home, or saw her grooving, between giggles, to the music as it played.

If she laughed, she thought, if she laughed and did not wince, the pupils would see that she was only Ayo and not the 'weird Black girl' they thought she was. And the next day she flashed them her brightest, widest smile. But no, that did not help things – the girls' tongues lashed her into corners with playground insults which she took, dazed.

She might have daydreamed then of returning with her mother and sisters to Ibadan, to get away from all the bullies and stop being Black. To be simply herself. A Nigerian again.

But in England were the smooth asphalted roads, those amazingly smooth asphalted roads which extended for miles, rounding hills, bridging rivers, making even vast cities approachable. (And with no cops pulling over cars to haggle for bribes.) Here pylons towered in smart long rows and water, hot and cold, gushed on tap. She knew never to take the water she drank or washed with for granted.

Ayo's patience with the Eastbourne girls, her wish to please them, was not limitless. Nevertheless, for a while she persevered. During a playtime she tried her foot at their hopscotch, since she liked anything to do with numbers, anything you could take away with you afterwards and play around with in your head. The distances between the squares. The optimal arc of the throw. She had thought the girls who usually played would join in, but when she tossed the stone on 1 and hopped up and down she saw that none among them would. Was she doing something wrong? While they were gathering round to watch she noticed their faces turn to masks of derision.

'You really don't get it, do you?' said one of her spectators.

They made her out to be Miss No-Mates. Finally, they turned their backs in a great show of cold contempt, so cold that it doused and numbed Ayo's desire to befriend them. But she never would forget any of their names.

When the boys walked into class, into maths, say, and saw her hunched over compass and ruler, only a few would give Ayo a shove, or a snarky look, and this made them an improvement on the girls. It just so happened that in those days she was reading *Alanna: The First Adventure* about a girl who passed for a boy. Alanna rode horses and fought knaves and did many other things girls were not supposed to do. Ayo felt an elating jolt of recognition as she read the story, though reading did not come easily to her. Words in print seemed never to remain steady on the page, they bulged and flowed every which way before her eyes and pulled and pushed her bobbing gaze along their currents; the effect on her was to read more slowly, more laboriously. Punctuation was a pain. For the longest time she couldn't take in capital letters or full stops, she couldn't work out where a sentence began and where it ended. And yet despite all this, she read Alanna's adventures with something rather like pleasure and imagined that she, too, might escape restricting herself to girlish ways. In class she was soon setting herself apart, sitting closer to the boys who, by and large, left her alone and some of whom, the spectacle wearers, could be as studious as she was. This was the beginning of Ayo's journey to engineering. Like Alanna, she would dare to do what most girls daren't. Advanced maths. Science and technology.

Stifled laughter could sometimes be made out from the boys at the back of the maths class. They were playing with their calculators, punching in 80,085 and giggling at the display.

Ayo didn't think 80,085 was lewd at all; if anything, she

thought it rather weighty and handsome – handsome as numbers went. Slot it into one of her graphs, and it would fit right in. She was aware though that, to several of the boys, numbers had no value beyond money. A pair behind her were fooling around, speaking their mind. Every daft, immature recess had its say.

'That's my future salary that is,' said one to his friend, showing him the calculator display. 'Eight thousand and eighty-five pounds.'

'*Eighty* thousand, Mongol,' the friend replied.

'Even better, man. Eighty grand a month. Sweet.'

'Yeah, right.'

'All right then, eighty grand a week.'

'Pffff.'

'A day.'

Girls, Ayo knew, also had their in-jokes, a sophisticated banter which could be thought far subtler than the boys', provided, that is, you weren't the target.

Most importantly, between the teachers and Ayo there existed a mutual appreciation. She liked how what they said in class was clear and to the point, because it came out of their knowledge. She paid them the compliment of listening closely. Her notes were always copious. They'd send their red pen up and down her classmates' homework, but on hers it almost never landed on an error. How often the Sokales' television set – turned off or down for a long-distance call to Ibadan – watched her as she lay on the living-room carpet doing her homework.

'Full stop,' a teacher would sometimes say. 'Don't forget the full stop.'

Ayo

Outside the air is already warm, and sparkly as you approach the water. Weather as fine as billed in the evening forecast. It has all the makings of the long, dry, peaceful summer days Ayo thrives on.

Before she goes to work, she likes to walk beside the river and have an hour alone with her thoughts. She prefers to hold them back from the people around her, for fear of being misunderstood. Or mocked. Likely both. She tried these thoughts once on her housemate but he could not wrap his head around them. He was for a time far more than a housemate. They met at uni, in Mr Rafiq's structural analysis class. Although he listened, and forced a straight face when Ayo detailed the lifelike, walking buildings she has sketched many times, he replied in a ribbing way that said that he could not credit them. Even he could not credit them. She learned her lesson; these days, in conversations, she sticks to safer topics. Contracts she has recently managed, budgets calculated, feasibility studies performed. The replacement of a weir in Maidenhead, the design of a fish pass in Oxford. Flood alleviation schemes like the one in Thatcham, a reservoir protecting three hundred homes.

She turns off her street and follows the Thames along the bank, as she has done on many mornings now for years. Every tree and reed is familiar to her, for the route is always the same. As are her brisk, rhythmic movements along it. Here is the patch of grass she always spots coming up at 7.12 a.m. And here is the iron bridge just before half past the hour. In the radiance of the sunlit water she is alive to every passing thought and sight. She feels seen. Seen as she truly is, or wishes she might be. Phil Collins is singing to her from the headphones. Got to love those reverberations.

Downstream of the bridge she enters the building of her

dreams, a building in perfect keeping with its environment. Tall, but by no means as tall as it can get. Glass and wood and steel, all proportionate. In the sun the place does more than shine. It gleams. Solar panels, naturally. Lots of windows. Rainwater tanks. No smoke because no chimney. Through the door and up she goes, treading on air, climbing it, each step higher than the last, and she isn't impeded by the lack of any stairs, for her imagination supplies them. As she strolls beside the meadow now (six minutes long) on the north bank, she continues walking through her mind, taking lefts and rights, from room to luminous room whose scent is of the poplars that she passes, without any thought for the floorboards not beneath her feet, the insulated walls not there, only for the interiors she imagines all kept cosy by the sun, and green with plants. Each room breathes, is airy. When the daylight moves out, the room responds by moving with the sun. The whole building moves according to the time of day – it can twist and turn and stretch. According to the weather, too, including the freak and extreme. Supposing floodwaters surge, the building draws itself up, gradually lowering its rooms, inch by dry inch, as the water subsides. And, what's more, it would shrink from noise. A flare-up of boisterous traffic, or a shouty crowd. The facade turns away then, or the whole building retreats a few steps, to keep its occupants undisturbed.

But what about the built-up areas? How would her walking, breathing apartments, or whatever they were, have any wriggle room in built-up areas? That was what her housemate wanted to know. He thrust up teasing arms to act out the apartment's predicament, seeking to elbow itself from a narrow row of terraces.

Ayo adopted a posture of defiance. She wasn't going to be teased or mocked into conceding. Tomorrow's towns and cities, she said, would look wholly different. Each place – home and school and office – would be conceived and raised in relation to one another and the surrounding landscape. Residents Hill and Lake and Bird would need to be consulted as scrupulously as anyone else. In which case, given sufficient care and planning and fellow feeling, plenty of space could be found for everyone. No? But by this moment in the argument she understood that her housemate only wanted to talk her out of such thoughts. He was no longer listening. He was waiting. Waiting to rebut. To get her out of ridicule's way.

These buildings she sees, has seen for years; they are far more real to her than castles in the air. They are, she feels sure, the future, whether hers or that of the world in a century's time. The question isn't if but only when.

She sees by the Caversham Lock on her right that it is almost ten to eight. Not long before the route leaves the river and takes her back to her street. A bite to eat, a quick wash and a change of clothes, and she'll be ready for the day ahead.

In university lectures, Ayo was taught the causes, in addition to the consequences, of flooding. She heard how the recent violent storms of 2012 had wrecked many homes and cost several Britons their lives. Scientists agreed that man-made climate change, if not the sole culprit, was in large part responsible. Picture it, the lecturer said, as greenhouse gas emissions grow, so does the water-holding capacity of the atmosphere. There is also more rain induced from the Atlantic to the British Isles by lower-pressure systems. Ayo pictured the rising waters breaking and entering through somebody's living-room window, drowning their heavy furniture and carrying off trinkets, letters, banknotes.

It was early on during the same civil and coastal engineering course that Ayo was called up in front of the room and asked to comment on a flow equation. She felt some of the forty eyes – young men's, almost all of them – watching her. Some perhaps admiring her work, her dedication, while others her blossoming curves and curls, the denim that hugged her narrow waist and which produced in her a sense of being held, of being safe. It was at moments like this, she knew, under a spotlight, that she excelled, when her energy, or intensity, could be regarded with respect and approval rather than considered 'too much', as some people said.

'. . . and here we can see that the imaginary part of the wave number is zero . . .'

The spotlight wasn't confined to university. It shone on her more brightly still when, before that year was out, she entered a local beauty pageant and won. She'd worked hard for her place and wanted to, counting calories and putting in the sweaty hours at the gym. Resolution and fatigue powered the pleasure she took in appearing up on stage. The other contestants were just as driven. Inveterate fundraisers, mountain climbers, volunteers. They spoke without apparent irony of preserving the planet, which seemed to be less cuddling koalas than it was picking up litter. They delivered their thoroughly prepared answers to the judges' questions, of the kind: 'Who is your role model and why?' When it was her turn to face the panel, Ayo remembered to slow down and not to speak so fast. She remembered her mother's complaining of the headaches her torrents of words and ideas could bring on. Anyway, this was only one part of the contest. What she longed for and dreaded lay ahead: the walk. But even in high heels she did not wobble. Like each of the young women, she had been well rehearsed. A severe voice – 'no, no, no', 'yes, more like that' – had put them through their paces. The bikini pinched her thighs and bottom. She breathed easier during the evening-wear round, which was of a piece with the hotel's ballroom. In a pink and silver dress with sequins, a tiara in her hair, feeling like a Bollywood princess strutting her stuff, Ayo dazzled.

Miss No-Mates had become Miss Plymouth.

Plymouth was a good choice for her studies (it had been that or Manchester, which she concluded might be too loud, too manic). A port city with expertise in all things marine, and numerous links to engineering. Also, and as importantly to Ayo, the city was a five- or six-hour drive from Eastbourne. She had reached an age where it felt urgent to leave the parental home far behind, since to leave was to grow up, and the further she went, the more grown up she might become.

It was during her studies in Plymouth that Ayo saw a dyslexia specialist. She was sent after a professor, not an unkind but an insensitive man, on reading one of her papers asked whether English was her first language. It happened that the specialist she was sent to see wanted to assess her for something else besides dyslexia. Autism.

She was, and she was not, surprised.

Another tab on Ayo's phone is no stranger to her fingers. It takes her to a page in the Encyclopedia Britannica that she began reading in Plymouth, when, far away from her parents and her Christian upbringing, she could explore the beliefs of her ancestors. Water, they taught her, is power, female power. The article she rereads is on Oshun, river divinity, goddess of fertility:

'The Yoruba people believe that the orishas were sent by Olodumare, who is considered the Supreme God, to populate the Earth. Oshun, being one of the original 17 sent to Earth, was the only female deity. The other gods, all male, failed at their attempts to revive and populate the Earth. When they realised they were unable to complete the task given to them by Olodumare, they tried to persuade Oshun to help them. Oshun agreed and brought forth her sweet and powerful waters, bringing life back to Earth and humanity and other species into existence.'

A wintry Friday, Ayo journeyed the width of the southern coast by train. Friends from last year's graduation class were waiting for her in Penzance, yet she spent the whole trip having second thoughts. She ought to have told them no. Thank you, but no. I can't. She had tried texting so, to begin with. London to Penzance would take a morning, and the return a long, tiring evening; she would be on the train twice as long as with her friends; it was simply too far to go for a day trip. But there had been some insistence from the friends, notably Tom, Tom being the one with the handy car and the gran who lived at Land's End – that and the rare loan of his parents' cottage for the weekend. Since Ayo's schedule would not stretch to a weekend, and she'd never had much of a head for excuses, she'd said yes to Friday. A timid yes. She fidgeted in her scratchy seat now and imagined the long reviving walk to come along the coast. The cold rain might hold off, the sun might put in an appearance. This image at least was heartening.

When she pulled into Penzance it was overcast and windy but dry.

At Sennen Cove they left Tom's car by the lifeboat station, near where the waves were crashing against the jetty. The walk was to Gwynver Beach and back along the clifftops. In better weather, on a hot summer's day, the footpaths frequently teemed with tourists; they would come from miles around on the advertised promise of cool breezes and matchless views. Today the friends were alone. Only nature accompanied them. From time to time banks of low-hanging cloud released gulls. Tom and the three other young men – civil engineering graduates to a T, all trim beards and red anoraks – in whose company Ayo trod a steep path down towards the beach, formed a protective ring around their friend in case she slipped. The wind off the sea brought an ever stronger taste of salt, of freedom, and when they reached the sands and approached the edge of the water the immensity held, mesmerised, Ayo's gaze.

She felt a new energy deep within her, sparking palpably through her, like the vigorous flash of lightning across a night sky. She felt irresistibly drawn towards the water and its promise of renewal.

The men could not believe their eyes. She was running, racing, to meet the receding tide. No testing with the tip of a toe or finger the temperature of the water.

This was not because she was larking around, or because she

wanted to dive in. It seemed stronger than her, this force that had surged inside her, pushing aside her reason, jolting her legs.

'Ayo!' shouted Max, who was the most phlegmatic of the group, his voice concerned. 'Where are you going?' He was running after her, they were all running after her. She was turning by then, coming back, but the high waves were faster. They immersed her. One moment the men saw Ayo, the next nothing but the roiling sea. Where, where was she? They cast their arms into the water and hauled her out onto the shore, shivering and stunned.

They assumed the walk was over at that point. But she took off her boots, wrung out her socks, and said she was all right to continue. Someone had a spare jumper, and Ayo removed her waterproof over-trousers and looped them onto her rucksack to dry in the wind.

As Ayo squelched along the beach, they asked her why she had chased the wave out so far and put herself in danger.

'The sea was calling me,' she said. She knew they would not understand. Nor did she, not entirely, not yet. But she could not suppress a glowing smile.

They returned to Sennen along the cliffs and went for lunch to the Old Success, where a crackling fire was going. One of Tom's old mates took their orders at the bar.

Warmed up, dried out, everyone then wanted to walk to Land's End as planned. Was she really certain she could not stay for the weekend, the friends asked Ayo afterwards on the way back towards the car. They were thinking of stopping at Newlyn to 'nerd out' at the ordnance datum level and grab some fish and chips. But Ayo was certain. The no was more confident now, it came easily to her. 'Thank you, I've had a wonderful day with you all, but no.'

Ayo

On the return train the hours rushed by.

I try to imagine
What the water wants.
There's no knowing
That has every answer,
No smart expert
With a stock response.
Only measuring tools
To find deep down
How far thoughts swim.

How far thoughts swim
To find deep down
Only measuring tools
With a stock response.
No smart expert
That has every answer.
There's no knowing
What the water wants.
I try to imagine.

Ayo hasn't often returned to Nigeria in the years since she left. The most recent occasion was her elder sister's wedding in 2017. It was a sumptuous, joyous affair, assembling family and friends from many places and time zones. It brought the dancer out in Ayo, but also, days later, as if in delayed response to her fervour, the need for time alone, chair drawn up to a window, chin on the heel of her hand. This land had hosted the two high dramas of her early years. The second, in 2001, was the armed burglary leading to her family's exile, in the course of which only courage and female solidarity had staved off the worst. But these virtues had hardly sprung out of nowhere; they were doubles of those found by the Sokales the previous year, early in the rainy season, on an evening which seven-year-old Ayo would never forget.

No one came that afternoon to collect her and her kid sister from school. They were sitting in their empty classroom (empty save for a teacher), a building on ground firm and high enough during the season's wettest days to remain dry inside. The rainstorm showed no sign of relenting, the drops increasingly loud and heavy, knocking and knocking, harder and harder, on the door and windows as if saying, 'Let me in!' Their mother had been caught in the downpour as she returned from a trip to Lagos. She had assumed the family's driver would collect the girls and bring them home.

It was seven in the evening when Toyin finally got in. 'Where are the girls?' asked her niece. An hour's journey on foot in the dark – for the street lights were down, the local roads washed out – awaited her. On lower ground she had to wade through murky water that came up to her waist. All around her, cars and rubbish floated. In the days that followed, several people would be reported missing.

Ayo delighted as never before in her mother's silhouette as Toyin clambered into the classroom and relieved the teacher. A dirty brown puddle swelled around her feet, and her blouse and wrapper were so wet they were see-through. Ayo had never seen her mother naked, or almost naked. For the first time she observed the outline of her mother's breasts, the roundness of her hips and belly. The shock of seeing them, mixed with relief, subdued the shock of having been marooned.

Toyin carried the sisters on her back and side, as she had once carried each in her belly. Ayo held on to her mother for dear life as they waded back through the drenching dark; she was afraid, and her fear was not far from despair. She would not understand until much later what she was witnessing, being subjected to: the drains absent or in disrepair, clogged with rubbish, the poorly thought-out roads built too close to waterways; decades of diverting a nation's wealth to line the Big Men's pockets.

Then at last the compound appeared, a fleck of light in the distance. Almost home. Her aunt and cousin whooping, 'Girls! You poor things!' as they hugged and kissed them and rubbed them warm and dry and helped Ayo into her green Little Miss Mermaid pyjamas.

She is her parents' blood, of course, but she is also water. More water than blood in fact. Over half of her lean body's weight is water (she has looked up the number on her phone); three-quarters of her brain and heart is water.

A lifetime's work to gauge these inner depths, to channel them; to conserve their strange and secret flow.

Danny

On the roof above the studio he stands and waits. All afternoon the studio floor is overbooked and surplus staff work where they can. A television camera stands with him on the roof, infinitely patient. The way it waits there it could be made of time. He – not so much. 'Action!' he shouts, and in short order the door to the stairwell opens and out step half a dozen spies, dressed in beige trench coats with their collars up.

Of course, they are not real spies, they are actors. Over-dressed, ironic parodies of the Z-movie secret agent, sunglasses and fedoras concealing their youth and gender (all of them, twenty-something). They are taping a sight gag for children's TV, they haven't any plan as such to follow. They improvise, entrusted to their instincts, for the director knows to keep out of their way.

Enduringly famous, several of them, from our perspective, by which I mean big-name, autograph-book-level famous. They don't know this, because they won't land their breakout roles for another year or more. It is Friday the thirteenth in September of 1974.

Autumnal, low grey-skied September in Toronto. With

every minute that passes four o'clock, it looks more and more like rain. Not the best day for filming outdoors, but what can you do? At present the actors race and leap and hop along the roof, which is a good twenty or twenty-five feet above the ground, maybe higher, until, near the centre-edge, they stand and put their backs to the skyline and the cars nosing down Yonge Street in the direction of the weekend.

Only a few japes more to go, the director thinks, and there'll be enough in the can to knock off too.

Now their heads are bobbing, ducking invisible rocks. And the director is happy, he is beaming, looking younger than his forty-odd years – much the same man as when he played the clown on a kids' show in the early sixties. Because all the comedy resides in the actors' energy: exuberant, zany, unpredictable. The camera is loving one of the biggest and youngest guys, the scene's powerhouse. Danny. Daniel Edward Aykroyd to the province's traffic cops, who will pull him over every now and then for speeding. See how he runs manic circles around the skylight! Watch the tall, burly whirlwind of his body as it gathers pace! Imprudently, he cuts across the skylight's dirty glass.

The director shouts to him, 'Keep off the glass,' but the honks of cars drown out the warning.

Danny plummets, in shock and gasping. In his haste he did not give the glass – its thinness – a second thought. He stepped on the pane, feeling it burst into shards, the murky void beneath swallowing him whole.

What happens to Danny turns the others on the roof to stone. All that falling could be the death of nearly anyone. They stare at the skylight with a pane now missing on one side, they peer down, down, into the storage room which a moment ago housed only light stands, and then someone, John Candy or Gilda Radner or another of the actors, starts downstairs to call an ambulance.

Supposing he hadn't collided with a water pipe on his way down, they will say afterwards. The pipe had broken his fall.

He is breathing, and his body is intact. The remains of the skylight glint around it, enormous shards like shark's teeth. Presently sirens sound, and Danny when he is hoisted onto the gurney groans weakly, 'Way to start my career in TV!' Quick as a shot, the ambulance man replies, 'You're going to be a star.' He pronounces this sentence in an accent of stunned certainty. 'We can fix arms and hearts,' he continues, 'but not heads.' To have come away in one piece from such a fall meant Danny Aykroyd's head had to be something very special.

The first time I heard Aykroyd and Asperger's in the same sentence I had just been diagnosed myself. That would have been back in the early noughties, which doesn't make either of us, Aykroyd or myself, any younger, but I still remember the interview well. It aired on National Public Radio, which I listened to on the show's web archive. To tell the truth, I came across the interview by chance. Aykroyd hadn't been in the news for a while by then, but when I saw the NPR link I recognised the name immediately. That goes without saying. For a period of about ten years, in the eighth and ninth decades of the twentieth century, he had been among TV and cinema's biggest stars. Being a child of the eighties, I grew up on his movies. Like just about everyone else, I saw him in *Ghostbusters* (whose original screenplay he wrote), with Bill Murray, their lasers trained on the slimiest – and funniest – monsters you could ever hope to encounter on film. So I listened with interest as the comic actor answered questions on his life and career, and almost fell off my chair when he told the interviewer about his Asperger's.

As a matter of fact, he hadn't gone behind that microphone expecting to talk about anything quite so personal. The interviewer, Terry Gross, had more or less hypnotised him, as he explained it later, with her excellent preparation and gentle questioning. Gross, too, was a little thrown; she seemed almost not to believe that she could have surprised Aykroyd into so rare a confidence. She wondered aloud whether he was joking when he said the funny-sounding word *Asperger's*, whether an interviewee like him, all alter egos, a jealous guardian of his private life, might only be teasing her listeners. But no. The word, which sounds like a bit of fun but turned out to mean what it means – mild, high-functioning autism – was uttered, it seems, quite sincerely. So that each time another interviewer would bring it up through the following years, almost in a whisper, as though it were a possible source of embarrassment, he replied in the affirmative. But he would not elaborate. The window on his mind had been tantalisingly opened, and just as quickly closed.

Upon embarking on this project in 2019 my idea was to speak with Aykroyd's early friends, neighbours, classmates and first colleagues, to learn more about those parts of his life the media had mostly missed out, his formative years, the ones that had made his extraordinary mind what it is. I didn't expect him to agree to talk with me directly. And so it proved. The way his cousin explained it to me, I got the impression that he found dwelling at any length on his inner life an ordeal, an ordeal like having his molars pulled. Which I could understand, even though I had never been reluctant to share my own experience of neurodiversity. As luck would have it, he grew up in Hull (as it was then called), Quebec, a place I know particularly well. In addition to Aykroyd's past interviews, I combed the local press archives, in both its languages. I sent out enquiries. I chased leads. I made many calls. The people who answered were all generous with their memories. Vivid insights and recollections, forty-, fifty-, sixty-year-old stories, they shared with me. A composite Danny began to emerge.

Peter Aykroyd had worked out west once. He had scouted locations for the National Film Board, in Manitoba, in Saskatoon, in Edmonton, weeks in advance of Princess Elizabeth's national tour. That was why his wedding to Danny's mother, Lorraine, took place out in Winnipeg, in September 1951. The king died that winter and in the summer Danny was born. Lorraine told her husband to get a proper job.

He worked then as a road engineer in Hull (and later behind a mahogany desk at the National Capital Commission). But Peter couldn't resist sneaking some televisual oomph into the home, in the form of a Philco set. How wondrous the new medium was: ballet dancers one hour, a quiz show the next – it radiated culture throughout the country. Alongside some less mindful 'entertainment' which was just as well; its programming was magnanimous. Slapstick to kill an hour agreeably, and then Liberace for the wife. And all those weekday shows, episode after unrelenting episode, as though everything in the world exists to end up in a show.

In the evenings Danny sat and fidgeted in front of the

porthole screen, and as the broadcaster read out the news the little boy repeated aloud every other headline. *The Prime Minister John Diefenbaker . . . in Malton, Ontario, the Avro Arrow was rolled out for cameras . . . yesterday's successful launch of Sputnik I by the Soviet Union . . .* Lorraine and Peter listened without batting an eyelid – the telly always had an echo whenever Danny was present; there wasn't an announcer, not a newsman, their son heard without mimicking the syllabic voices.

Adequately informed, Peter rose from his chair and switched off the set, and Danny along with it.

Lorraine would have much preferred to wean Danny from the screen; she would have preferred to see him outside, playing sports, like other people's boisterous boys. But knowing his son, Peter couldn't see that happening. He had another idea: why not make him a microphone like the one TV announcers use? A toy to occupy the small hands more pleasingly than, say, flapping. He sawed up a beat-up hockey stick he had, and wrapped the toe of the blade in a black ball of duct tape and then dropped a length of string from the heel, curly as wire, conducive to a little boy's imagination.

Someone might speak to him, as he sat watching this or that show, and he would seem miles away. Even on a hot day he'd warm in his hand the glass of milk that his mother or, sometimes, his grandmother gave him. A grown-up's commands to scrub dirty palms, comb hair or remake the bed, coming when they did from the other side of the little screen, he could blissfully disregard. He seemed to have ears only for the characters. He could have listened all day to the one called Friday, Sergeant Joe Friday, although the detective entered living rooms every Thursday (and later, Tuesday) – for the bright, clipped things he said. This and other voices too he absorbed, exhaled back, the better to merge himself with them, dissolve in them, become them. Light as a voice. And as free.

Only ... sometimes the set resolved not to work, as all things electric are prone to do, and the static supplanted the voices then and would have left Danny in angry tears. His father consoled him with a bedsheet. Hung in the basement, it became a movie screen on which Peter projected rented reels. *The Ghost Breakers* starring Bob Hope, and the Bowery Boys in *Ghost Chasers*. Buster Keaton and the Keystone Cops. His father's son, Danny goggled at the old square cars onscreen, how they vroomed and spun and knocked walls and barns, even themselves, gleefully to pieces. Cars, it seemed, could take all manner of liberties in this world. Oh, to live like a car!

Every morning Peter drove his Ford Sedan to the heart of the capital, to the beehive of government offices.

He was very tall, prematurely bald and a snappy wearer of ties. Back in college, in Toronto, he'd been on every student committee going, and that same great sense of duty, or work ethic, kept him constantly caffeinated, prodded him to bring his work home in the evenings, stacks of paper reshuffled by the swing of his suitcase.

His suitcase saw many cities. He was much in demand as a speaker at Rotary Club dinners, and this champion of urban planning could have been a preacher, so impassioned was his every talk: Canada, land of green pastures and a future of peace.

The Aykroyds' house stood apart from most other homes in the town, on the edge of Gatineau Park, whose new-built roads, cut from Precambrian rock, wended between the lakes and valleys, ferried visitors by the million every year, and owed their existence to Peter's engineering. (Five years in the making, those roads, Danny's preschool years.) Young Danny had his bedroom in the basement under the garage, waking to the engine rumble sparked by his father's key in the ignition. It's time, the always punctual key would inform him. Time for school. Get up. Danny gave a consenting groan, less obedient to the key than to the anticipation of warming oatmeal. So cold outside. And dark. His bleary eyes adjusting, shadows in the room turned to cowboy hats, plastic guns, comic books, model tanks – all competing for space with the biggest shadow of them all. With its Westclox clock and folders and colour pencils, the bedroom table had become homework territory, though he didn't need to sit very long there. Probably he spent longer dressing for class in the morning than setting down right answers in the evening: fiddly pairs of socks and long johns and corduroy trousers, a thermal T-shirt underneath shirt and woolly sweater. The mitts, like the scarf coiled round his neck after breakfast, were woolly too. Mukluks encased his feet, a ski mask his face. Then he zipped up the garish snowsuit.

The light outside was weak when Danny left the house – big enough by the age of seven to fend for himself, so his parents thought – and he had brought along a torch, or perhaps a long twig, just in case. Behind the house stretched woods of pine and spruce, alive with wolves and bears. It was sleeting, the sough in the pines came clearly to him, and the pungent earth felt very near, recalling the dump trucks and the lumberjacks which his father had long supervised, and taken his son out in all weathers to see. Danny had heard the workmen and their tools before he could see them. The digging and the sawing and the motor-turning. Those sounds grown familiar soon entered his lexicon, and Danny when he set out now for school repeated them, here and there, to no one in particular, speaking in fluent spade and axe and chainsaw. Or as an engine revving.

First he skirted the woods and clambered down a steep slope of rock, and then he came to a clearing where there lay a creek, and under the narrow, wobbly plank that bridged it, waist-deep freezing water. Danny threw his knapsack across before negotiating the plank. He tried to put out of his mind the nipping memories of falling in. He stretched out his arms, for balance. Little, tottering steps.

Presently the trees thinned away and he followed a path across the highway to a neighbourhood considered bad. He was deep in thought, dominated by an incessant flow of ideas to the exclusion of everything else. Unaware of the figures that began to circle him, in an ever-decreasing circle. He was talking to his boots. Either that, or his rigid gait, or the cosseted dressiness of his clothing, had stirred up this pack of lads – and soon, through his snowsuit, Danny felt their calloused fingers jab his arms, ribs and chest. His mask they attempted to rip clean away. Holding fast to it, he fled into the school.

The plain red-brick building on the corner of Davies Street hasn't changed much since Danny's time. It is now a remedial learning centre for poor working-class adults, after being an elementary for mainly poor working-class children. Many of the children sounded as Irish or Scottish as their folks, McThis or O'That. Today's pupils in this part of Gatineau (as Hull is now called) have inherited the names but lost the accents. They attend newer, gentler schools. They wouldn't recognise a leather strap, or the spool or skipping-rope handle which in fact was a nun's clicker, designed to quell a class. One click, open your readers. Two clicks, pick up your pens. Girls are no longer a separate species, stuck in their own rows and serge-green tunics. Even so, the clannishness of children remains. The surveillance, the strict division of those deemed 'in' and 'out'. Durable as any plain red-brick building.

So the school didn't assimilate him, far from it. Everything reminded him of how strange he felt within its walls. The John Wayne swagger of the older boys. The incomprehensible drone of the Lord's Prayer, like a TV's glitchy audio. In the hubbub of the playground he felt his shyness like a deformity, like a misshapen head. The other children thought him a nerd, as Aykroyd would say years later, a geek, as he would say as well, although the kids in Hull, Quebec, would have put it differently back then. A drip, more like it, a square. A funny boy, their parents might have thought, and whether they meant funny ha ha or funny peculiar depended on their mood and perspective. Neither a friend-magnet, then, nor a teacher's pet.

The women teachers at Our Lady of the Annunciation – for they were all women – were short and stout, wearers of talc and corsets and tortoiseshell glasses – in a word, matronly. The same firmness of curves, slowness of movements, blackness of hair, a suspicious black that seemed almost blue: so many emblems of their authority. No malarkey would any of them take. Nor sides; they bestowed their knowledge impartially, on the earners of gold stars and red marks alike, on those who talked dialect at home and those who didn't, on the aspiring typists and future factory hands. And on Danny. He was in a category all of his own.

A head taller than the other children when they stood alphabetically in line for class, too conspicuous, not knowing what to do with his hands or feet or gaze. He wouldn't necessarily meet his classmates' eyes. And that was just the half of it. His sprawling, left-handed compositions read like nothing the teacher would have seen (if the first drafts of his future screenplays are anything to go on): long but ingeniously digressive, branching out into a hundred backstories, each scene and character more inventive and more surprising than the last. This was a boy who liked nothing better than to loiter in encyclopedias, who knew the insides of atoms and the capitals of all the provinces, who sounded like he'd swallowed his father's civil engineering manuals: 'shale', 'theodolite', 'lateral load'. And just wait until you got him on prime numbers or the solar system, talking so fast he would have made Sergeant Bilko proud, Lucille Ball smile. You couldn't stop him then. His boundless inquisitiveness made him exhausting to teach. I don't know if he was oblivious to an adult's impatience, wanting to squeeze answer after answer out of the Miss, or whether he found some questions simply irresistible. In which case he could hold them back no longer than he was able to hold his breath.

How many people live in France? How many towns are there in France? Is Paris the size of Ottawa?

He was like the air-raid siren that sat over the girls' side of the playground (the kind that, twenty years later, Aykroyd would put in a movie atop his Bluesmobile): you never knew when he might go off. And one day Danny went further and demonstrated his own powers of disruption. Picture the following. The teacher would have been explaining something to the class in her usual roundabout way, maybe tripping over some stat or date – she must have seen an impatient look come into his face – and then stopped and said, 'What is it?', and other disapproving words. The rows behind him put down their pens as he said, switching to his TV detective voice, 'All we want are the facts, ma'am.' From anyone else, it would have seemed to her the height of impertinence. Very likely she had not gotten the joke, and was unprepared for the children's reaction. The boys, studious a minute before, fell into a laughing match. They laughed at the top of their lungs, unthinkingly, daringly, competitively. The teacher shouted over them. That's. Enough. Out. Of. You. Young. Man.

Had it even been a joke? Had he known what he was doing? You couldn't be sure, coming from a nature like Danny's. The shifting voices and odd flights of fancy, next door to the shy bookishness, made him an enigma. Deliberate or not, the scene in the classroom altered Danny, so that he came into some new knowledge of his resources, the ways of diversion, attracting the pupils' attention to characters put on and then slipped free from. And indeed for a while, maybe a few days at a time, the boys forgot to harass him at recess or to be cold towards him. They let him be.

The teacher, in turn, thought up her own harmless subterfuge. Her breath smelled of the humbugs for which she regularly dispatched Danny to the local sweet shop, thereby buying thirty minutes or so of peace for her and the classroom. In this way, Armand Monfils, the confectioner, relieved her for half an hour in the afternoon. Her desk drawer teemed with humbugs for as long as Danny was in her lessons. (Sometimes one of the other boys would be all sweetness and light until the humbug errand was his, the thirty carefree minutes away from class were his, and Danny, mightily peeved, knew he'd remember Ricky Hollingsworth till the day he died.)

Some days, when Danny could have been away at the sweet shop, he had to remain instead on the premises. Miss Nellie

Bradley, the headmistress, would want to see him. He was a regular in her office. Miss Bradley, who was the aunt of the early-grades teacher Miss Sirois, and who sometimes asked her niece about the Aykroyds' boy and heard her answer that he was quite a handful – a pain in the neck, Miss Sirois, who had a soft heart, did not say – Miss Bradley, though not herself exactly a laid-back lady, would pull in a few colleagues and have Danny entertain them. The cigarette smoke would get so thick as to sting the boy's myopic eyes. Ask him to do Hilly, one of the ladies would whisper, and Danny would imitate so precisely their colleague's tone and pitch that it was as if Mrs Preslawski weren't at that instant several classrooms down, but standing there in person.

He could be quiet as well, when the circumstances required it, so quiet you wouldn't even know he was there, all eyes and ears. During the last hour of lessons, for example, when he feared being held back, kept from his cartoons (though they were far from his mother's idea of a good viewing habit – he'd catch them on the sly when she wasn't around), and also when the school's television set rolled into class. Danny was old enough by then to know not to echo back what he heard, so that the only voice in the room came out of the screen.

The boys in the school films looked and behaved nothing like him. They wore wrinkle-free plaid shirts in winter; horizontal-stripe T-shirts in summer. They bought thoughtful birthday gifts for their mothers; wrote friends in distant towns fountain pen-pal letters; watched pucks pushed and whacked across hockey rinks. Like his father and younger brother, they were invariably called Peter. He was a Danny in a world of Peters.

Danny had never had a friend like him.

Theirs were the first names called when the teacher took attendance. Aykroyd. Chitovas.

He was the rare boy who would play with Danny during recess, risking the jeers of the first and second picks for ball teams, a skinny boy with small eyes and hamster cheeks, Danny called him Chich after the puppet in *Chich in Cartoonerville*. Modest, unpromising looks, but enveloped by the glamour which an early brush with mortal peril gave him.

Chich's father had saved his son's life, and those of his three daughters. Nick Chitovas went to bed one night and woke to find his firetrap of an apartment up in flames. Chich was an infant at the time, like his sisters, and remembered nothing of his father's howls in the family's Quebec French. Nothing of being grabbed with a sister and hurtled into the frozen street and the crowd of onlookers, his father like a man possessed, in a frenzy of urgency and heroism. Nothing of his father braving the blinding heat again and returning, long minutes later, with the other sisters. Nick Chitovas's face, it was said throughout town and down the years, was black with soot and his hair smouldering. And with every retelling, the fire grew fiercer, the smoke blacker, the shouts and sobs louder. Nick Chitovas's hair went from a meagre wick to a halo of dancing flame. Up to here, the tellers would say, waving their arms high above their heads. And Danny, witnessing neighbours recount the tale, was entranced by the theatrics of a good story.

Lunchtimes found Chich and Danny setting off for the woods' edge, leaving behind the school and highway. The retreating snow smelled of humbugs as they ran along a stream, shooting baddies or lassoing Indians. Or else they retired to the woods to play hide and seek. Danny was the best hider Chich had ever known. Chich would close his eyes and count to twenty before tiptoeing among the pines and hear only a chainsaw splutter, or a dumpster's ignition in the distance, and the next thing he knew the chainsaw was calling to him or the dumpster driving his way, louder and louder, and then nothing. Silence. Danny could do silence too, the eerie silence among the trees that canopied the forest floor. 'Danny, where are you?' Chich would shout and the woods echoed back, *Danny, where are you?*

Another game they played was cops and robbers, alternating the role of culprit. Danny loved reading or hearing or thinking about crime; the police, and the people they arrested, exercised an equal fascination on him. As far as he was concerned, being afraid of outlaws was for grown-ups. He had the softest of spots for outlaws. Perhaps he envisioned them, but this is speculation, as brethren – comrades in alienation, fellow strangers to polite society with its unfathomable and countless rules. Rules that, always changing, could get the better of anyone. Capricious. One day's parking space was another's traffic violation. The same beer served at 1.05 a.m. in Quebec would be bootleg in neighbouring Ontario. Danny thought a lot about such things, about right and wrong, good and bad, as policemen did. And criminals, apparently.

Let's go see the jail, Danny said to Chich one Saturday. Probably he told him about his father's crossing the threshold, now and then, paying Christian visits to the convicts. The convicts were housed out in the woods, not far from the Aykroyds' home, so if one or more escaped, as happened sometimes, they might almost run into the two boys playing. The men never did remain out for long. All those bedsheets tied into a makeshift rope, for a few days, or only hours, of freedom.

The boys picked up their bikes and rode bumpily in the direction of the jail. Chich lagged behind Danny; his nerves were catching up with him.

'Chich, we're here!' Danny said as he jumped off his bicycle.

'Sacramento!' Chich exclaimed, braking. 'Danny, do you see them?'

'Raccoons. Raccoons in cages, half a dozen of them,' Greg Chitovas, now seventy and a Bell Canada retiree, told me by phone. 'Who knows why the prisoners kept them there. For company I'd have thought.'

A man's paunch blocked out the view. The paunch belonged to one of the guards. 'What have we got here?' he said unnecessarily. The boys skedaddled.

And when a colleague asked the returning guard what that had been about, the guard, with a shrug, said, 'Nothing, just kids. Nick Chitovas's lad and some wide-eyed pal of his.'

A new toy. Danny shook it, but not roughly. He held the Magic 8 Ball as he held any book, with an abiding reverence for all that he did not know. Question after question he asked it, questions he'd intended for his father.

'Might humans communicate with extraterrestrials?' ('Ask again later.')

'Is time travel possible?' ('Signs point to yes.')

'Do many other dimensions exist?' ('Better not to tell you now.')

Danny

When the 8 Ball's answers didn't satisfy, he took his questions to the family bookcase, or to the bookshelves in the old clapboard farmhouse in Frontenac County, where the Aykroyds spent their summers. Hours of sunlight to read by. He read the contents of his ancestor's shelves. Books that were alphabetised, or otherwise kept tidy, by his father who liked to quote his Latin primer: a place for everything, and everything in its place. Venerable-looking books like *The History of Spiritualism* by Arthur Conan Doyle, handed down from his father's grandfather, and stacks of back copies of the *Journal of the American Society for Psychical Research*.

He learned about ectoplasm, a kind of gelatinous and whitish substance, so these books and quarterlies stated, used by spirits to materialise their likeness. Ectoplasm is exuded through a medium's nose, mouth, ears or belly button during a séance. It can be handled, smelled, occasionally photographed for posterity. The light of day causes this transient substance to vanish. When Danny asked his father whether he had ever seen ectoplasm or perhaps even touched it, his father, every inch a believer, replied with regret in the negative.

The original owner of these books, Samuel Aykroyd, had been a dentist at the close of the nineteenth century, a time when the trade's tools were like so many instruments of torture, and pain relief nonexistent. Whether Dr Aykroyd ever practised what he read about mesmerism remains an open question. Perhaps he didn't hypnotise his patients. Perhaps he didn't swing the gold fob of his pocket watch before their eyes. Whatever was his professional interest in these theories, they persuaded his family to mingle their Christianity with spiritualism.

*

Peter Aykroyd told Danny and his brother about a Sunday evening long ago, when several cars had driven up to the family's farmhouse. Big Dodges and the like. This would have been in the year 1929. Seven-year-old Peter, crouching in the bushes, observed the visitors from a distance. They were sitters, his grandfather told Peter afterwards, and the word would give them a special dignity in the young boy's mind. From behind the bushes he crept inside the cellar at the back of the parlour. He had never known the household in such a state of animation. The men and women were walking in now. From where they came, he didn't know – the big town to the south, Kingston, or somewhere in that neck of the woods; children, in any case, didn't ask a lot of questions back then. The women smelled of perfume and mink coats. His grandfather opened the door to the parlour and let the group ceremoniously file in.

The parlour had a square wooden table in its centre and an old stone fireplace, and shelves of his grandfather's books. Through the cellar door he heard the sitters pull out their chairs and take their places around the table, the drapes being drawn, and the medium demand who was there that day from the great beyond. He heard the curious noise eight or more adults make when they hold hands and breathe in harmony.

Before long, someone came through from the other side. All Peter could say for sure was that the voice groaned so low and deep it wasn't a voice. In any case, not a human voice. One of the medium's spirit guides was communicating through him: a Chinese fellow by the name of Lee Long who'd lived during the Ming dynasty, or Blue Light, a prince, or so the sitters believed, from Ancient Egypt, or perhaps the Native American called Broken Arrow – whoever it was spoke up and invited questions from the darkened room. One of the sitters asked about a departed relative, and Lee Long – or Blue Light or Broken Arrow – said the beloved was in a better place, and when this response induced a gasp of joy, and relief, from across the table, the spirit proceeded to share memories that the sitter recognised.

Sometimes a séance would turn up nothing, Peter conceded to Danny and his brother; no usable information from the dead would be forthcoming, which the sitters attributed to a negative, or worse, a sceptical thought crossing one or more of the minds present around the table. Danny felt he'd be incapable of any such thought. He couldn't get the medium's many voices out of his head.

Danny ought to see a professional person. That would have been the advice of the headmistress. Most parents of the period wouldn't have heard of a shrink for their child. But Peter and Lorraine Aykroyd were not most parents. Both widely read, university educated, with a high regard for science. And Peter, back in his National Film Board days, had worked on documentaries commissioned by the country's mental health association.

It was at a child guidance clinic – a common euphemism then for child psychiatry – that Mrs Aykroyd set out her son's difficulties as best she could. They had worsened in the past year, she told the psychologist, ever since her son had entered sixth grade and Mrs Marier's class. This teacher wasn't tyrannical, but she wasn't understanding either, always ready with a frown, and teacher and pupil had never gotten along. She was a strict and mean lady with an angry wart right between the eyes (this description would have been Danny's). At first only a few heated words, her punishment would swiftly make itself felt:

a rap of her ringed fingers, or of a ruler, to the boy's temples. Every other peep out of him seemed to merit the strap (which never missed – Mrs Marier hadn't made the teachers' bowling league team for nothing), until he had ended up dreading school altogether, he who had aced most classes outside of sports. Indeed, thought the psychologist, who would have seen the boy's academic reports, Danny Aykroyd was very much his high-achieving parents' son.

First observations. Speaks in a staccato fashion. Hair: unruly, dark. Eyes: one green, one brown, furtive. Weight: satisfactory. Barks or grunts like a small animal when overstimulated (according to parent's testimony). Can raise a smile or a laugh without meaning to. Or perhaps he does. Talks for Canada. Repetitive to a fault. Narrow interests: guns, police, ghosts. All things mechanical. Excellent memory. Trouble at school. Involuntary eye blinking, shoulder shrugs, twitches. Doesn't fully grasp social niceties. Has potential to progress.

He submitted willingly to having his mind probed. The psychologist wanted to know why women and children should be saved first in a shipwreck, how many pounds made a ton, where was Chile, what did turpentine come from, which part of a thermometer in the illustration shown was missing.

Danny didn't need to be asked twice before he gave his answers.

He recited numbers, assembled jigsaws, led his pencil tip out of mazes. In rows of squiggles he detected a chosen symbol: a hexagon, say, or a hoop like a flat tyre.

He would have been asked to draw a man, a woman, himself. How he drew himself, or the woman for that matter, is anybody's guess, but for the man I have my idea, more than an idea in fact, though I cannot be certain, so let's just say that what he drew that day required many strokes of his pencil and blanched the knuckles of his left hand.

He may have been shown ink blots to comment on. Ink blots that looked like hungry timber wolves. He may have been asked to play a game of word association. That would have been tricky. He wasn't one to say the first thing that came into his head. There never was a first thing. There were always so many things, and all of them coming up for attention simultaneously; no sooner had he found the word for each than more besides rushed to replace them.

Great was the psychologist's wonder when the boy's results were totted up. The test scores identified him as highly gifted, no question about it.

In my mind I picture the parents hip to hip in the waiting room, and the psychologist, after having called them in, seeing Mr Aykroyd, all six feet something of him, and thinking, The man's a giant. The boy takes after him.

After a number of sessions the learned doctor would have found the name for Danny's stubborn eccentricities. The psychologist, based on all the information I possess, talked of childhood schizophrenia (as the autistic spectrum was still called then in some parts), a diagnosis originally brought to Canada by German doctors who had fled the war. An excess of imagination, it was thought, leading the child inwards.

Only later would autism become associated with blankness, or incapacity. No longer associated with imagination, let alone artistry.

Danny would attend counselling, as prescribed, for his tics, his anxiety, over several years.

As for the rest, the psychologist had an idea that theatre might remedy shyness. Had the boy any experience of the stage?

'As an altar boy,' answered Mrs Aykroyd, unless it was her husband Peter.

Then there was the time he sang for the school, the parents recalled. It had been for the school's St Paddy's celebrations. Danny, flanked by a pair of classmates on the flute and the kazoo, had belted out 'McNamara's Band' to a standing ovation. Or so the Aykroyds' son, long afterwards, would describe it to a reporter in an article for the local press.

He would have been on his best behaviour. Stick to the lyrics, make no waves, hold still and upright throughout, since success, he knew, promised a smile from the headmistress and his parents' relieved pride.

There was something else the Aykroyds might have thought to mention. Camp Echon. And here my imagination is on the firmest ground, for I was able to locate a photo of Danny, aged eleven, in the pages of the *Ottawa Journal* dated 2 March 1964. In this first article to take the slightest interest in our future star, his name is misspelled 'Ackroyd'. A grainy black-and-white photo shows a tall pre-teen boy, with thick lips, riveted eyes and a monk-like thatch. He is hugging a trophy to his cheek as he gazes at the reporter's camera with an air of utter and deserved self-satisfaction. He had bested five hundred boys to win the Best Camper trophy the summer before.

I imagine the boys around the campfire listening open-mouthed, their gooey marshmallows speared on sticks left dangling in the air as Danny told stories to give his audience goosebumps – stories about séances in a farmhouse, and prison escapees on the run, and infants dragged gasping from an inferno's maw by fathers with flaming hair.

Theatre, the psychologist concluded, could do the boy a whole lot of good.

Lorraine Aykroyd had learned to tickle the ivories as a girl, danced in tutus and dressed up in drama class. Peter Aykroyd hadn't learned piano or worn a tutu or gone in for school plays, but he had a thing called presence: on his Rotary Club tours he'd bring a hall to a hushed silence simply by appearing at the lectern. Yes, a bit of theatre, why not?, they thought.

And so every Saturday Danny rode the bus along the Ottawa River and the Chaudière Bridge into Ontario, passed the Supreme Court and Parliament Hill, before alighting a stone's throw from the Ottawa Little Theatre.

The theatre air seemed to agree with him. It inflated his lungs, swelling his chest, not without infusing him with motes of lint and make-up, particles to make a trainee thespian sneeze, although they only sweetened his existence. As did prancing around a stage. Throwing his voice to the stalls. The Mrs Mariers of this world would not approve. Bliss.

He had entered that magical space where misfits recover their value, where even the most peculiar turn to pearls: encores for the klutzy and the closeted, lead villain roles for the short and bug-eyed, and Broadway plays in which the frail and wrinkled make a good living reciting a character's dying words.

Danny's drama teacher was a slim, boyish man, with long-lashed eyes and the same soft face he'd had since age ten. And appearing so, children loved the sight of him for he looked anything but teacherly. He was now twenty-three. His name was Brian Gordon, never Mr Gordon; and if any of the boys ever called him Flash, it was always with affection.

Turn-taking games and playful exercises in imagination were the chief characteristic of Brian Gordon's classes, which were based on techniques invented by Peter Slade. The Englishman had been writing and lecturing on child-centred drama for the past decade by then, and fathered a field that thrives to this day: drama therapy. The earnest intention, rather than treating theatre as academic fodder, was to make children actors in each other's lives, capable of measuring the different effects of their words, roles and actions on another person. A drama teacher, or therapist, had only to nurture this awareness through the structuring of play and the setting of scenes in order to enable every child to flourish.

When Danny came out of the theatre, he felt more alert to the life that pulsed all around him. Before Brian Gordon he might have kept his head down, lost in thought. He might not have noticed the passers-by on the streets or the passengers on the bus as it rattled homewards. Now he saw things differently. There they were, the very same theatre games that he played, in the prim gossips who matched their faces to their listener's reaction, in the gestures of candour, of encouragement, of exaggeration that animated hands, in the gaits that stiffened as a cop or a clergyman passed.

Lorraine Aykroyd, though she tried seeing her eldest son through the psychologist's eyes, hearing his theatrics through Brian Gordon's ears, was perplexed. She did not see in him the same great promise or creativity. She saw turbulence. Her son needed a firm hand – that was the reverend talking – to straighten him out. Yet while she agreed she also knew that Danny needed more than discipline. He was coming up thirteen. What might the future hold for someone like him? He didn't seem destined for a white picket-fenced house, a nine-to-five job.

It was at this time that she thought of sending him to the Pius X Minor Seminary in Ottawa. The priesthood would offer him cover for his oddities. After all, she might have thought, men of the cloth need not observe society's conventions; their cassock exempts them from paying a mortgage or raising a family. To the suggestion Danny's father, devout like his wife, a walking Bible even, agreed, although I doubt he ever really considered his son priest material. No matter, since the seminary doubled as a boarding school.

Danny was admitted and boarded Monday to Friday. The Aykroyds had vouched for their son's deep faith, describing to the director his weekly bike rides to church to help at Mass.

Mass. There was a lot of that now at the seminary. And Fathers so obese they slept with bricks beneath their bed, and others, in class, who tossed chalk and worse at dozing heads, and the Sisters of Saint Martha, in their habits, who cooked for the cafeteria.

Latin was compulsory. Headache-inducing conjugations and declensions. The boys ploughed through Julius Caesar's *Gallic War*, deciphered the daunting verses of Catullus. Unavoidable, too, the mud and shoves of field sports. *Mens sana in corpore sano*. Danny wouldn't have cared for those. He mightn't have cared much for the dorms either, the bedsheets coarse and scratchy. Monday nights would be worst for homesickness.

He might have gone to the window then. The night, black and white with blizzard, was a vast television screen on the blink.

All that said, the seminarians didn't have it all bad, for some nights after lights-out they would creep out at ten and catch the end of a film at the Auto Sky drive-in. And the nuns clucked around them like mother hens, plying them with milk and cookies they had baked themselves, and raising chuckles with their dry sense of humour. The Fathers, meanwhile, offered plenty of material for imitations. Danny did an excellent Father Baxter. The stoop (unkind tongues called the Father Quasimodo or Modo Man), the chalk-catapulting, the shrill cry of 'Smarten up, jokesters!'

Other boys who tried to do the Father ended up doing Danny doing him.

And then there was the library, well run and well stocked, where Danny would find every kind of book to read to his heart's content, and his head's, his reading tastes being, to put it mildly, eclectic: everything from woodwork to motorbikes to home economics, as evidenced by the many checkout cards that soon bore his signature. The library walls held spacious long windows that bathed the room in brightness; when Danny opened a book's covers, it was like sunning himself with its pages.

Inevitably, the sixties worked their way into the seminary. 'Blowin' in the Wind' was sung at Mass by the younger priests. Attitudes to long hair, or certain kinds of clothes, were softening. Soon Fridays became dress-down days, when the boys could abandon their shirts and ties for jeans and T-shirts. Danny once came into class in jodhpurs, a leather flight helmet and aviation goggles. I have seen a photo of him in them. Another time he could be seen in long white gloves with a police whistle on a lanyard, loudly directing foot traffic in the hallway connecting the classes.

He would do odd things like that. Not to make a spectacle of himself, for he had a shy boy's stutter in those years. Or, rather, not only for the spectacle. Most likely, he was still learning to measure his effect on other people, and testing the boundaries of adult patience. Other misbehavers in the seminary weren't indiscreet in the same way. More streetwise, they'd make sure, say, not to smoke within smelling distance of the Fathers. And they knew better than to shout an explosive word, like 'bomb', on a class outing. They knew themselves to be boys vulnerable to cause and effect, and expellable. Not Danny. He always seemed to be teetering on the edge of something.

The same summer that he wrapped up his third year at Pius – maybe thanks to all his mother's prayers – the mood in the Aykroyd household, and the country at large, was celebratory. This time next week, Danny thought, he would be fifteen and Canada one hundred. Canada and Danny shared their birthday: the first of July. Appointed to the Centennial Commission, his father had had a hand – or even both hands – in organising the 1967 celebrations. And this evening, just a week before the big day, the Aykroyds had something else besides to celebrate, for on this last Saturday in June, in the grand dining room of the Hotel Eastview, Edward Gougeon – Eddy to his grandson Danny – and his wife were ringing in their golden wedding anniversary.

Danny could have done with Eddy back in first grade, marching into Our Lady in his red and black Mountie best, impressing the teachers, putting the fear of God (or, at the very least, of the Crown) into his grandson's bullies. But Eddy Gougeon had already retired from the Royal Canadian Mounted Police by that time, and everything Danny knew about his grandfather's career had come to him by way of anecdote and the sterling-silver medal for long service he'd have seen somewhere displayed.

Danny was giving consideration to becoming a cop himself, a Mountie like his mother's old man, minus the horse. He would pass the Ontario Police College course in Aylmer and ride a Harley-Davidson Police Special and people would call him Constable – no, Sergeant; no, Staff Sergeant Aykroyd. He'd go on and on about bylaws and know just what to say and when, and the interrogation room would teach him all the conversational skills he'd ever need.

At some point in the evening a chic and stately woman rose, looking much like Lorraine Aykroyd, only younger: Helen Gougeon, Danny's aunt, who gave a toast to the happy couple. Danny was fond of Aunt Helen, who was quite the character, as well as something of a celebrity. The newspapers carried her weekly food column complete with photo (the photos taken at various angles, in each his aunt wearing a different outfit and hairdo, as though she were a dozen women in one), and her recipes had found their way into a cookbook, *Helen Gougeon's Good Food*. To think of Aunt Helen as a maker of books! It made sense, considering her way with words, which was as precise as Danny's mother's, who was an executive stenographer, but also witty. She was always the life of the dinner party, Aunt Helen, holding court even as she sliced a tearjerker of an onion, an opinion on everything.

The discreet waiters, bearers of wine, or perhaps champagne, threaded between the tables.

'To the Gougeons!'

Lucky Eddy! Danny thought that he too would one day have a long-service medal, and a wife of fifty years, and all the other satisfactions of the retired policeman.

The night Eddy died, Danny dreamed that Grandpa Gougeon walked by a lake, waving. It was the same lake he'd seen many times before, through the window of the parlour in which his ancestors on his father's side had long conducted their séances.

The next morning the telegram from Ottawa reached him in Toronto, where he was working at the time. He looked at his calendar. It was 25 September 1975. He would be starting on a new TV comedy show in New York in the next fortnight. NBC's *Saturday Night*.

He had plenty of reasons to dislike the Big Apple. The crowds. The red tape. The dog-eat-dog world. To say nothing of the loud and frilly clothes; New Yorkers seemed obsessed with their clothes. He had no time for stuff like that; most days he'd throw on his motorcyclist's black jacket that he teamed with black boots and gloves.

But whenever Danny saw the blue-collar streets reminiscent of his native Hull, the rust and brick and dives and flophouses, his attitude towards the city softened. He admired the phantoms of rising steam above manholes that caught his eye. And the energetic beggars, some legless, yet amazingly swift on their wheeled boards, with whom he rode the subway. From there he went on to 30 Rockefeller Plaza, where the elevator carried him up eight floors to the NBC studio.

What did New York make of him? Hard to say. A wacky

youngster (he was twenty-three) from the Canadian sticks, perhaps. Or one of those ingenious freaks big cities attract and spit out every now and then. He raised eyebrows when he passed TV executives, smelling of motorcycle leathers – Danny, not the bigwigs, who I imagine gave off an odour of cologne. To his greater discredit he wouldn't schmooze. He could just disappear on you, in the middle of a party, amid a showbiz who's who, without a word to anyone. Some in the industry were already calling him Frosty the Robot, because he could come across as impassive off the air, insensitive without his lines and cue cards, that and his stilted way of talking.

But his flair, the magic that was his when he called up the farthest-fetched comic characters to vanish inside, was undeniable.

A character had come to him one suppertime when he was eating with the show's producer Lorne Michaels and cast mates at a friend of a friend's apartment. He said that a funny thing had happened once long ago at his Aunt Helen's lake house in the Laurentides. The visit in question would have gone by like all the others there during his boyhood, without leaving any particular trace in his memory, had Danny, that evening, not wandered into the kitchen just as his aunt was finishing the preparations for supper. She was holding a great big fish away from her by the tail, the belly flashing silver with scales, the useless gills gaping, the glassy eye watching him. Dropped into a blender, the fish dissolved instantly in swirls of white-pink mush.

'Wha-what happened to the fish?' he heard himself stammer. His aunt turned away from her Cuisinart and looked at him.

He asked why the bass had been blended, scales, bones, gills and all. She answered that it was for a bouillabaisse she was making. Then she exclaimed his name: 'Daniel!' she said, perhaps to reassure him, or to admonish his walking in on her, and repeated the word bouillabaisse as though it were explanation enough.

All the while Danny reminisced, he made fish-dropping gestures and imitated Aunt Helen's face and her voice as she said 'Daniel!' and 'bouillabaisse'. His host that evening, Paul Simon, the popular singer, unruffled by most things, nearly gagged on the laughter which had been rising in him as Danny spoke.

Danny thought, if I can get a laugh like that out of Paul Simon ... and he wrote up his skit soon afterwards and produced it on the show.

He received mail from viewers after the Bass-O-Matic sketch. A letter in angry-looking handwriting left him especially agitated. 'Last night's show,' said the viewer's letter (as best as I can reconstruct it), 'was an outrage. How anyone could think to treat a fish like that is frankly beyond me.' To which Danny answered with a missive of his own, long and digressive, on the properties of mass and matter, a point-by-point, even painstaking, reply that he could have summed up in a sentence: 'Dear viewer, fish or humans, we are all living on borrowed atoms.' Over four seasons he ate and drank and breathed these TV sketches, each a week's consuming labour of writing, rehearsing, cutting and polishing, performed live between commercials for laxatives, pantyhose and Timex watches, and generally applauded by the critics. And quoted still, and savoured by fans, half a century later. Some of the best stuff the show ever put out – some of US comedy's most enduring creations. He played an old-movie cop, a psychiatrist, an extraterrestrial in suburbia. And then there were his sketches based on the most arcane minutiae: the schedules of American freight trains, the finer mechanics of military bomber planes, the callipers and armatures on mail-sorting machines.

There were days it could be hard for Danny to keep it together, the viewing figures stakes ever high, the long days in the studio claustrophobic, the metronomic constancy of rehearsals both reassuring and intimidating. The occasional loss of self-control visited on him by the stress could prove spectacular: a fire alarm smashed to shards, holes that yawned in walls where he'd thrown them repeated punches.

Rehearsals could be exhausting. He would often find something amiss. He fussed over the most ordinary of props – in one scene, a typewriter on its desk. If the typewriter prop was electric (preferably an IBM), if its keys could all clack in proper typewriter fashion, if ink to turn out a good few sentences was present, if a spotlessly blank sheet of paper was set and ready, then and only then might the rehearsal proceed. This thing on the desk he thought an insult, unworthy of the sketch, something to be swept aside. Which is what he did, swept it crashing to the floor.

To cool off he'd retreat to his dressing room and dip into one of the heavy books, on computing, or history, or some manual, he was forever reading.

Some nights he'd ride out for hours on his Harley-Davidson Police Special. He loved driving on a back-country highway on a quiet night with the mist rolling off the fields, smelling the thickness of the manure spread on the land, hearing the ping of insects striking his helmet. It brought him back to the times in college he'd be taken out at midnight in a friend's car and ask the driver to open the sunroof and stand and feel the wind whip and surge around him.

Other nights he and a cast mate would catch a movie, nothing too touchy-feely, with plenty of car chases and at least one shootout. And afterwards he would tell anyone who would listen that the, say, Smith & Wesson 36 revolver shown resembles the Smith & Wesson 38, which has a shorter barrel, and the K-22 Masterpiece MRF, which has a similar checkered-walnut stock.

His name was increasingly known by then and he got offered his first movie roles – it was during this time that Danny starred in *Love at First Sight*. A no-budget Canadian film shot in nineteen days by Rex Bromfield, a friend's brother; Danny played a blind man who elopes with his sighted sweetheart to Niagara Falls. The excursion to the Falls made up for the poor showing at the box office, and the reviews which were mixed. The green water steamed and churned and roared and stilled the flow in Danny's head. Between takes he'd recalled admiringly the tightrope walker in the nineteenth century who strolled aloft many times here. Much like himself, he thought, ever stepping out without a net in sight. He liked to remember the walker's exploits: the perspiring accomplice piggybacking on the walker's shoulders, the egg fried and eaten in the centre of the wavering rope. He aimed for the same gravity-defying poise.

Reporters started to wonder where this wacky Danny guy had come from. But they had trouble reaching him. He refused to leave an address or number with the channel's PR. He spurned interviews for TV, for the radio, for the papers.

He had no gift for introspection. Pinned down on set, he would offer the bare facts of his background, give an honest reply to the hack's questions, and shake hands as he left. That much he did. But he wouldn't open up.

Danny's starring in *Saturday Night* (soon renamed as *Saturday Night Live*), his subsequent fame and fortune, might never have happened – he might have wound up, say, in an Ottawa Police uniform – had it not been for his unlikely friendship with one Valri Bromfield.

This is how the two came to meet. Sometime in the fall or winter of 1967 or thereabouts he performed a prank too many at Pius. He was thrown out. The headmaster told his father, 'This isn't a school for clowns. There's a school for clowns in Moscow.' He did not go to Moscow. He went to his third (by my count) local all-boys Catholic high school, St Patrick's, and one day, strolling down the warm stretch of underground tunnel connecting St Patrick's and the theatre on Notre Dame's campus, he caught the ear of a girl in rehearsals for the theatre's latest play. The girl was a recent Notre Dame alumnus, three, four years older than Danny, meaning that she was nineteen, and Danny fifteen.

As she got closer, Valri saw a thinnish lad with a monobrow and a mop cut, a lad rapt in his thoughts, a lad who appeared oblivious to her and the other students he passed. He seemed to be conversing with the walls of the tunnel, telling them formulae and facts and all sorts of Latin-sounding words. She listened closely to him, savoured the curious music of his words, let their strange power sink in. This kid is something else, she thought, a brain like that doesn't come along very often. She approached him, typically bold. He hadn't noticed her presence; she walked right up until he stopped and looked at her and fell silent.

They hit it off. Not in a boy-meets-girl way, for Valri made no secret of being attracted to girls; more a meeting of minds. She had his knack for imitation and his outsider's edge, and though their friendship was no older than the school's tunnel was long they talked there, underneath the classrooms, as if they were the only two people there.

They lost no time performing together. Danny played Schlegel the circus master to Valri's Rosalie in a high-school production of *Carnival*, and at the end they came out and bowed to the applause of the full house, or perhaps of the half-full house, or at least of the scattered teachers and parents present.

Comic sketches they kept to themselves, at least to begin with. She made fun of netball coaches and lissom Miss Popularity types, and he made fun of truck drivers and gun-toting cops, and both made fun of the old. The older, the funnier.

Some days, after class, Danny and Valri rehearsed together in a neighbour's living room, or at the Bromfields', at a safe distance from any antiques, where for an hour or more they bounced imitations off one another, non-stop, all manner of gestures and accents (French, German, Irish, you name it) that Danny had overheard on the streets or lifted from a TV or radio show, shows like *Hogan's Heroes*, references that any North American might catch. They brainstormed oddball situations, swapped gags, refined a sketch – at home he was filling his notebook with alternative punchlines.

They'd be the next Nichols and May, she sometimes day-dreamed, getting first billing on Broadway, *An Evening with Danny Aykroyd and Valri Bromfield*, and releasing an album of their sketches: *Danny Aykroyd and Valri Bromfield Instruct Teachers* or some other title like it.

Destiny. That might have been Valri's or Valri's and Danny's thought – a class roll call would have placed them side by side: Aykroyd. Bromfield.

They were always together. They seemed inseparable. But Valri was older, and before long she felt her feet itch. She wanted to see the world. She was done with studying and with student productions. Perhaps she promised Danny she would write, and perhaps she did, during her time overseas as an au pair, then a Digger Pugh circus girl, postcards wishing he were there and postmarked Mayfair, London, and other cards or letters, with Spanish stamps.

She wasn't abandoning him. She would be back, sooner than he knew, and turn his life upside down. Danny never would have guessed. It's over, he probably thought, I won't ever see her again.

In any case, Valri went to Europe and Danny went to college.

The year was 1969. The university was Carleton, in Ottawa. Long-haired, bell-bottomed students met in each other's digs to remake the world. They pulled the American troops out of Vietnam, impeached Nixon, buried imperialism. Danny didn't fit in with the revolutionaries. For one thing, he hardly looked the part: bowl cut, tie and jacket and horn-rimmed specs. When he talked politics, he detailed the ins and outs of British Columbia's Social Credit Party platform. Or he referred to ten-year charts of Canada's prison population, the flow of recidivists, the sociological theory of illegitimate means – all things he was studying. And while he was 'on', all intensity and statistics, the students might invent or remember some appointment to run along to. Only the more intrepid, or less adept at making excuses, feigned patience.

He found the night more welcoming. Just across the river from Ottawa, Hull's nightlife was more or less a disproportionate number of watering holes awaiting the 1 a.m. crowd, the drinkers who crossed the border from stricter, soberer Ontario, some spoiling for a fight and others looking for company, some slaking their thirst and others shaking on under-the-table deals, the terms of which remained entirely verbal.

Other nights found him at a coffee house called Le Hibou, or The (Night) Owl, a favoured haunt of blues-loving students and government workers, and from behind a table spread with a red-and-white chequered cloth and an empty bottle of Chianti for a candlestick, he listened to the musicians up on stage (who called him up once to keep the beat in the drummer's absence), their plaintive sax and vibrant strings and songs of hard knocks, of lost men trying to find their way, of lovers trying to fathom a lady's heart, songs which, in his state of mild inebriation, mellower for the two or three quarts of placid beer inside him, moved him deeply.

Thereafter he'd raid the album collection of a fellow Carleton student, Doug Tansley, and play Ma Rainy and Blind Lemon Jefferson and Mississippi John Hurt, among others, on Tansley's Dual 1209 turntable.

Sometimes he'd get up mid-record, pat his jeans and ask for a pencil, and small whitish balls of paper would exude from his every pocket, fragments of an old school essay, a garage receipt, crumpled library cards, on which he drew character after odd character in no time at all, mafiosi among them, with shades and concealed guns.

He got involved in the university's theatre troupe, Sock 'n' Buskin, graduating rapidly from stagehand with ten thumbs to sometime actor. He was in *The White Devil*. He was in *Iphigenia at Aulis*. He had a small part in *Colours in the Dark*. With time, the other troupe members got to know Danny's tastes. Pirandello? Absolutely. Ionesco? Yup. Chekhov? Not so much.

He was the only memorable thing in *The Death and Life of Sneaky Fitch*. He was the town doctor, a Southerner, drinking in a saloon. The young woman opposite him was a parody of a barmaid. She spoke through the gum that she pretended to chew. And when Danny heard her lips smack, her tongue clack, over and over, instead of remaining in character, downing his fictive beer and saying his next line, he was seized by a desire to imitate the girl's gum chewing. Chomp, chomp, chomp, went his mouth, smack, smack, smack, clack, clack, clack. How did the audience respond? They burst into nervous, or surprised, or simply rapturous laughter.

(Deep down, the 'barmaid' thought: that's me seen through. I'll never be an actress. But, as she'd tell me decades later, she ended up getting her Equity card all the same.)

Danny surprised his troupe mates even more the time he showed up for a housewarming party. He was amiable enough offstage, but not what you'd call outgoing. His eyes were hidden behind sunglasses, his body in an old and baggy double-breasted suit, of the sort found in Salvation Army stores, and no sooner had he arrived than he shut himself in the bathroom. The other guests stood and mingled and suddenly heard a sound like a buzzing, only it wasn't, it was a harmonica playing the blues. Nobody knew Danny could play. They listened intently, watching the bathroom door. And when Danny stopped, and stepped out, into the silence made by the pocketed mouth harp, he said nothing but joined them for a few drinks and a bite before seeing himself out.

You wouldn't bump into him outside of class and rehearsals. He wasn't one to hang out much. More and more, he absented himself from the life of the college.

There was one spot on the campus, though, where he might reliably be found. If you headed behind the social sciences building and down the lawn to where the river ran – there the water reflected his sitting frame. The Hog Back Falls, like a miniature Niagara, could be heard rumbling in the distance.

The winter of 1971–72 in Hull and Ottawa was something else. The inhabitants had hardly known snow like it: houses with snow up to their eaves. One of the homes snowed in was the Bromfields' place. Valri, long back from Europe, was inside; so, too, was Danny.

They were not improvising, as they used to do, not then at least; their conversation was serious. Valri did most of the talking at the start.

I can't see her sounding Danny out. That wouldn't have been her style. She wouldn't have said, Toronto might be a fun place to live. Instead, she would have said, 'Ottawa's no Toronto, Danny! What are we doing here? Too small. Too conservative.

Boring. Boring. Boring. Toronto's where the action is. A city with contracts to sign and fan bases to build.'

She had always known that her days in Ottawa were numbered. She was going places. Namely, Hollywood. She saw them both in a near future on the stage and the big screen, their names in lights. They'd be famous – did he hear her? Famous.

Hearing her talk like this, Danny was flustered and angry. He almost wished she had never returned. His home was here, his family was here. He was close to graduating. All her dreams of rising he countered with premonitions of a fall. Hadn't she the foggiest idea how tough it was to 'make it'? Didn't she know how many wannabe comics and actors clogged every agency going? Countless youngsters dreamed of landing a movie or a TV series or a commercial or at least a walk-on part in some regional theatre production, precisely none of which panned out ninety-nine times in a hundred, you had to be realistic. Miseries they'd earn then, with nothing left for blues albums or motorcycle parts. Count him out.

Their argument lasted for days, until finally his resolve cracked and he fled from the house, out into the blowing snow, tearful and imagining he'd thumb a ride home though no car came.

So Danny quit his studies and followed Valri to Toronto.

The summer after leaving Ottawa, Danny toured with his own satirical revue called *The Pickle*. A small restaurant-bar in Montreal hosted him and two other young debutants. Neither the flyers distributed nor the advert in the local press roused any great curiosity, much less a crowd. The first night, they were maybe a dozen, counting the three performers, to show up. The second night, the audience and slender takings were halved. The third night, Danny and his colleagues played to a single couple, whose attention quickly waned and who began fighting mid-show. There was no fourth night.

Between auditions he worked hard, adding mail truck driver and runway load tester to his CV of blue-collar jobs (he'd also been, at various times through college, a warehouseman, road survey crewman and rolling stock operator – inventorying had been his favourite part of the latter). He made enough to pay the rent and bills and put beans and beer on the table, and he could always scare up the dollars for a treat.

But there was more to it than the money. The roles. In a job, he was somebody. Somebody who knew just what to do and say when, for instance, at Toronto airport, he stepped out onto Runway 006 and said, 'All right, please close all air traffic, we're bringing the trucks in now.'

Valri and Danny were soon on stage in one of Toronto's gay bars, joking their best to garner applause the way the drag queen before them – his name was Pascal – had done. They were still learning. Take pauses, a thing most people retreat from in ordinary conversation. Danny and Valri, improvising, learned to trust a pause when it came. Not to tread on it. Because that was often where the laugh was.

It was something Brian Gordon could have taught him: speak only when what you say improves on the silence.

When Chicago's Second City improv theatre set up a Toronto branch Danny and Valri were both recruited for the troupe. (John Candy got in the same day.) The branch was a few blocks from their lodgings, an old fire hall where they now performed their late-night comedy. The hall had been converted not long before into a club and restaurant. They would do a set with the other members of the troupe, and then go out and improvise, 'Okay, ladies and gentlemen, give us an occupation.' Some guy yells out lawyer. 'Okay, give us a place.' Bathroom in a bus station. So they'd do a scene about a lawyer between buses taking a leak.

Some nights the audience would be small and tough, the type that sits on their hands – you might not get a snicker or a chortle out of them, forget about a good honest belly laugh. And some nights an empty seat would glare at them and a fumbled gag would throw someone momentarily off their game, but they would always pick themselves up and soldier on until the end.

Afterwards they would stay backstage and compare notes. Valri's stony silence announced an imminent dressing-down. Danny, you stank tonight. You weren't on, I don't know what you were thinking. She lashed him with reproaches. He wouldn't bristle, he wouldn't shout back, he would just stand there, head hung, taking it.

The other comedians were impressed, though – Danny had the goods, he was the real thing. Lightning quick with an IQ way up there, ever ready to take a sketch fruitfully off-tangent. And who but Danny would imitate a deadpan radio man saying of a crop circle: 'The cows had their lips surgically removed'?

But some had the impression that there was never any personal chemistry with Danny. He didn't listen to his partners on stage as the others did; he fixed on specific words in a sketch, either written in advance or just that moment improvised, and on the flood of associations they set off inside him. And there were times, in mid-performance, he'd turn abruptly rigid. Besieged by a familiar anxiety, he'd look down at the boards and see only a choppy sea of molecules beneath his boots, no solid ground, and for a second feel dizzy. Then he'd slam his whole body down on the floor and make the boards groan reassuringly. 'Good stage that,' he might say. 'Sturdy.'

It was common knowledge that Danny had meltdowns. Say or do the wrong thing and he could lose it, every modicum of his calm. Nobody wanted to be there when it happened.

The manager at Second City couldn't help noticing that Danny did not observe the performers' dress code; he was always in his poor excuse for a pair of jeans – from where he'd been knocking about with his motorcycle all day, they were frequently scuffed and dirty. That displeased the manager, who wanted Danny to think of the paying customers and smarten up.

Not wanting to make a big deal of it, he'd asked one of the comedians to pass on the message. Everything seemed to be going fine. But when Danny heard his colleague say 'jeans' and 'management', he turned red and trembled like he had a fever. Then he exploded. The manager knew where he could go and put his shirt and slacks. He paced about and blinked fast and shouted something about blowing up the building, and perhaps it was just as well the manager was out that day.

Still, the next time Danny went up on stage he wore a clean pair of trousers.

505 Queen Street East, Toronto. A growly male voice was coming out of the jukebox.

'What's this?' said the American.

'A local blues band,' answered Danny. 'You're from Chicago. You should know all about that.'

'I'm more into heavy metal. Crunchy guitar riffs.'

'Well, then, listen up.'

This exchange happened sometime in the small hours, a night in February 1974, at the counter of Danny's bootleg joint (or illegal booze can, as he also called it). The place catered to the city's night-shift waitresses, truck drivers and cops.

The American sat at the bar nursing the beer Danny had served him.

Danny pulled up a stool beside him, this squat American whose friend he had been for all of four hours, and observed him closely: the driver's cap, almost hexagonal, and the white scarf he'd taken off once indoors, the white cable-knit sweater, like the sweater Steve McQueen wore so handsomely in *The Thomas Crown Affair*, the feet shod in sneakers – totally under-dressed for Canada, Danny thought.

The two had met backstage at Second City. This new friend was scouting for talent for the *National Lampoon Radio Hour* and, in Danny, he had his guy. Danny demurred. It wasn't that the show didn't pay right, that wasn't the problem. Danny was not a man to change course if he could help it. He had money here in Toronto, a stage, and this place to keep him busy.

The man warned him not to become complacent. He left Danny his number.

The rest was destiny, or so Danny must have thought after their successful TV audition in New York the following year. Destiny's roll call. They were to be the best of friends, closer than Aykroyd and Chich, and Aykroyd and Bromfield. Aykroyd and Belushi.

It's 7 p.m. here in Paris, 11 a.m. British Columbia time, and I'm sitting at my living-room table, shouting at a blank computer screen. Danny Aykroyd's first director, Trevor Evans, can't get his webcam to work; and, now eighty-five years old, he is a little hard of hearing. But he can see me just fine, he says from his home in Penticton.

It was Trevor behind the camera on the afternoon Danny fell through the skylight. He rode in the ambulance with him, accompanied him home afterwards. He had first seen him at Second City, where he was searching for his cast. *Coming Up Rosie* would spend three seasons on Canadian children's TV programming, the first one with Danny.

Before *Saturday Night Live*, the sitcom was Danny's great experiment in front of a camera. The channel's tapes were wiped and only seconds of footage survive online, but Trevor was able to locate several episodes in his personal archives to send me. Unseen in almost half a century.

Trevor told me that Danny repurposed his 'Scottish Fedex driver' character at Second City for the show, turning him into a screwy send-up of a by-law enforcing building superintendent. A stickler for rules. Inmates at the Toronto jail, having only two channels, tuned in, and Danny received letters from some of them in care of the studio. I'm guessing these letter writers spotted things that would have been lost on the other viewers, the preteens and their parents and even the cast and crew, up to and including Trevor – how, for example, the name Danny chose for his character, Purvis Bickle, was a nod to Arlo Guthrie's 'Motorcycle Song' with its 'pickles' and 'motorsickles', so that the mere sound conjured up fast wheels, canyon leaps and the liberating smell of gasoline.

And I imagine the tenderness Danny felt towards these first

fans of his, as he read their smudged and clumsily constructed sentences, the words following their own rules of grammar and punctuation and spelling, 'goest', say, for ghost, like something out of his father's King James Bible.

'Kids like to be scared,' Trevor said, and he had encouraged Danny to make use of his special interest in the supernatural. One of the episodes he sent me was called 'Mousetrap for McTavish' and the plot was pure Danny. Purvis Bickle tasks one of the building's residents with taking action photos of his pet hamster McTavish. The hamster escapes into the walls, where it scratches eerily and chews through the wires, causing the building's lights to go out. In the near dark, Bickle consults a Ouija board but the result is Gaelic-looking gibberish. He mistakes a resident dressed in a chef's whites, giving off puffs of flour, for a ghost. 'Ectoplasm' he says to describe the scene – probably its first use in broadcast history.

So very young, this Danny, but already verging on fame, the many names for himself – Beldar Conehead, Elwood Blues, Ray Stantz – he did not yet know he would make.

Acknowledgements

I am deeply grateful to all those who shared their stories with me for this book: Vaughan Bowen, Kana Grace, Warren Hines, Eve and Billy Megargel, Amanda Tink, Ayo Sokale.

And to the following whose public life and career have been a further source of inspiration: Naoise Dolan, Cédric Villani, Dan Aykroyd.

Ed Lake believed in *Nine Minds* from its beginning and I would like to thank him for his confidence and encouragement.

Fran Fabriczki and Seán Costello provided valuable editorial feedback, while Fran Barrie, Izzy Everington, Georgina Difford, Alison Alexanian and all the staff at Profile Books/Wellcome have worked hard to bring these stories to readers.

My thanks, as ever, to my agent Andrew Lownie.

Special thanks to my family and friends, near and far, and to my husband Jérôme Tabet.

Béatrice Bonhomme generously gave her time for the narrative portrait of her nephew Cédric Villani.

Laura Crane and Kara Rodano kindly corresponded with me for the narrative portrait of their colleague and friend Kana Grace.

I am grateful to the following for their memories of Dan Aykroyd: Peter Blais, Lynn Blin, Rex Bromfield, Greg Chitovas, Linda Dompierre, Will Dunlop, Jayne Eastwood, Trevor Evans, Joe Flaherty, Al Franken, Guy French, Jim Girling, Linda Goodwin, John Gribbon, Mitzi Hauser, Rick Henderson, Ricky Hollingsworth, Beth Kaplan, Frank Kenny, Dianne Lanoue, Linda Nolan Leeming, Don MacKinnon, Blaine Marchand, Mark McGowan, Mike McNamara, Edward Myers, Laraine Newman, Glenn O'Brien, Gay Osler, Gerry Potter, Catherine O'Neill Salki, Curtis Schnobb, John Stocker, Rudolf Stussi, Doug Tansley, Sharron Timmins, Pej Vong.